DaRLa's
Last Kick at the Can

By S.D. FORSTER
& Diane Foley

www.darla-darling.com

Darla's Last Kick at the Can
Copyright © 2017 by S.D. Forster
All rights reserved.

www.darla-darling.com

ISBN 978-0-9958622-0-3

Love comes to those who still hope after disappointment, who still believe after betrayal, and who still love after they've been hurt.

~Unknown

INTRODUCTION

A CCORDING TO PEW RESEARCH, there are over 91 million people using internet dating sites and over one-third of them are over fifty years old. An astounding number, as I assumed searching and finding love was mainly for the young.

This book was written to share my story of my search for the man of my dreams, and to hopefully inspire other women to have **One Last Kick at the Can!**

When a person is left alone due to divorce or the death of their spouse, or just plainly dumped, facing the reality of a new future can be overwhelming. The loneliness can seem brutal. Everything has changed. Close friends have their spouses and their own routines. There is a huge empty space. How do you find a new life for yourself? I believe you should take some time to reevaluate yourself. Remember the old days when you had dreams? Dreams that perhaps were not fulfilled due to your unselfish devotion to family life?

I believe age is irrelevant. You are still you, that fun joyous person, and with a little encouragement you can find yourself again. This is the time to think about you. Catch up with old friends, dare to travel, Paris, New York, the Grand Canyon … or it can be someplace intriguing and close to you.

There are so many positive things to do. Learn more about your country, maybe learn another language, or be inspired to write a book like I have. Share the wonderful and maybe not so wonderful stories of your life. You are important and your contributions are important.

And do you know what? You are amazing and have survived many of life's hardships, and as a result you are a better, stronger and more resilient person.

Remember all of this about yourself when you decide to sign up for online dating. You only wish to meet an equally amazing person, as this will most likely be the person with whom you will share the rest of your life.

With that I say congratulations for having the courage to take the next big step in your life. Don't forget to bring your sense of humour with you.

Darla
December 2016

CHAPTER 1

I HUNG UP THE PHONE AND STARED OUT THE WINDOW. That had been Darla. Crying her eyes out. She had fallen in love with a nuclear physicist and had given up a great life in Vancouver. Literally had left everything behind to go and live with this fucker in Edmonton. Now, after two weeks, he had told her it wasn't working. Two bloody weeks! She had sold everything, even her beloved bust of Beethoven. She had been over the moon; so excited.

Charles had seemed a likable sort. Not the nutty, absent-minded professor type. Maybe more "nuclear physicist"—he had more of a mathematical-equation approach to life. He was a big handsome guy. You'd call him a hunk. Twinkling eyes, the deep-blue ocean kind and a brilliant mind. But apparently he had no staying power. He had left a marriage of thirty years to be with Darla, and his two sons had ganged up on him and told him, "It's us or her." And so ... goodbye, Darla.

Mind you, the sons were both in university and I would have thought would have a more mature understanding approach to life, but as I like saying, kids have too much power these days.

Darla had sobbed and said he was taking her to the Greyhound bus station and she was taking the midnight bus to L.A. Sounded like the title of a song. I wished she was coming home. She could have stayed with me and we would have worked out the next move. We were good at that. Darla and I. Working out moves. When you've been a single mother, like we both were, and pretty broke most of the time, you not only learn the moves, you figure out the whole bloody chess board. We had shared our lives for the past five years, living around the corner from each other. If I leaned out my apartment bathroom window and Darla leaned out her apartment kitchen window, we could wave at each other. We did that when we were tipsy and silly and talking to each other on the phone.

Now she was going to Los Angeles because she had a dear friend there, a French-Canadian woman called Ginette, and was too crushed to come back home and face everybody. After all the goodbye parties, the little engagement shower, and the big sendoff chorus from work: "Whoopie ... you've hit the jackpot, a rocket scientist!" Who could blame her?

I had asked her why didn't she go to the UK and visit her family in London, but she had said, "Are you kidding? I can't let them see me in this state."

Darla was my dearest friend, and I was going to miss her like hell. I poured some red wine into one of the

Mexican blue wine glasses I had bought at Darla's garage sale and checked the clock. Three hours to midnight.

Darla sat on the Greyhound bus looking straight ahead. She was damned if she was going to wave goodbye. Look at him! He was standing there, cool as a cucumber. Sort of like a Bogart silhouette wearing that damn trilby hat of his. Even had the gall to lean in and ask the bus driver to look after her. The *irony* of that. She refused to look at him or talk to him while they waited at the bus station. What a nightmare. She felt like she was in a dream. She had known for the last week something was wrong—he had been distant, kind of unplugged. They still made love every night though. Oh yes, he was not too unplugged for that. She could almost hate him if she didn't love him so much. Why in hell hadn't he talked to his sons and resolved his situation with them before he had asked her to come and live with him in Edmonton? They acknowledged that their parent's marriage was a mess. Acknowledged that their mother was difficult but ... they didn't want their father loving someone else. She held back the tears until the bus pulled out of the depot then sobbed uncontrollably into a wad of Kleenex. She felt her heart was breaking—oh God, she would never survive this. The way she felt right now if there was a cliff or a bridge she would gladly do the jump. Her broken body would be featured in the Edmonton Sun. That should make the asshole choke on his breakfast Wheaties.

She blew her nose and stared at herself in the bus window. A middle-aged woman with a mess of blonde hair, swollen blue eyes, and a reddened nose stared back. *Jaysus, Mother of Mary, she looked a fright.* And to think she had actually consented to live in that ice-frozen, god-forsaken horror of a city, Edmonton, all for the love of a man. It had been averaging -26C the whole two weeks of her stay; it was a miracle her nipples hadn't succumbed to frostbite and simply fallen off.

The bus seemed to stop every few miles and let people on and off. After a while, Darla fell asleep. She woke with a jolt to find an elderly lady sitting down beside her. The woman held a small brown purse and a bible in her gloved hands. Darla stared suspiciously at the bible, and the woman smiled sweetly back. Wrinkles everywhere. "I carry it everywhere with me. The Lord is *always* besides me wherever I might go."

Darla grimaced back. Just what she needed. A bible thumper. *Please do not start talking to me!*

"So where are you heading?" the woman asked.

"Los Angeles."

"Oh my. A long journey then. Are you American?"

"No. Canadian."

"On holiday?"

"No."

"Oh. So you are going to live down there?"

Darla gave the nosy old bird her best Johnny Carson stare. "I've just been dumped by my boyfriend. I'm going to L.A. to get over a broken heart and to try and forget the asshole." *That should shut her up!*

The elderly woman gasped. She thrust the bible into Darla hands. "Pray to the Lord, my dear. Pray! The Lord will deliver you. Just ask for His blessing."

Darla snorted a frustrated sob of despair that quickly morphed into a guffaw. *Was there no end?* "Oh God," she choked.

"That's right," the old woman encouraged, "just start talking to Him."

In the end, the old girl had been born on the prairies, growing up on a sprawling, isolated cattle ranch in Manitoba. Her family had raised cattle for three generations. She had married the son of a neighbouring cattleman and then along had come BSE.

"A brain-eating disease," Ethel informed Darla. "It hit in 2003 and destroyed the cattle business in Canada. Just like that! Bovine Spongiform Encephalopathy. Oh yes, I know that name like it was the back of my hand. Took out our herd. Even my husband's favourite horse. Killed my husband along with the cattle. My dear Jim died of a broken heart. It's a terrible thing for a man to see his whole life's work wiped out just like that. That's when I turned to the Lord."

Darla took Ethel's hand and squeezed it gently. "Oh Ethel," was as all she could say.

They sat in silence for a while, chatted a little more, and then to both their surprise the bus turned into the Calgary Bus Depot. Darla had to change busses for the U.S. and Ethel was going on to Rocky Mountain House. Time to say goodbye.

Darla hugged the old lady, who stood at the max five feet tall. She smelled of lavender and a whiff of mothballs, and if truth be told looked a little insane standing there in the middle of the Calgary Bus Depot clutching her bible, her red hand-knitted toque pulled down over her ears. A voluminous purple wooly scarf was wrapped around her neck so only a strip of her wrinkled face showed, but Darla knew she was smiling.

"I'm so glad you were on my bus, Ethel," she said, and to her surprise, Darla realized she meant it.

"Now bide my words, dear. Everything will work out. You'll see. Something wonderful around the corner will be awaiting. Just have faith." Ethel's muffled voice was barely audible.

Sweetgrass, Montana. Next bus change. Darla snuggled down and fell asleep thinking about Ethel's story. Her husband's horse had been called Starlight. Such a pretty name. She slept fitfully at first and then became used to the bus stopping and starting. When she woke up they were pulling into the United States border crossing. A few minutes later the bus pulled into Sweetgrass its very self. She checked her cell. Charles hadn't phoned. Had she really thought he would? She switched the damn thing off.

Darla stood staring, pulling her coat around her. Hell. If this was Sweetgrass, there wasn't much to it. There was a general store. Maybe she could pick up something to eat there. An Englishman she had noticed on the bus, the only other person to get off, wandered in behind her. He was underdressed for the weather in a tweedy-looking suit. No gloves. No hat. He looked like that snobby Brit type who would say, "Oh gosh. Would you care for some crumpets and tea?" They both came to a halt before a sign that said, "50% off ammunition when you buy beef jerky!" *Really?*

"Hey ... I guess we're truly in America." Darla shrugged her shoulders at the Brit with a look that said, "Can you believe this shit?"

"My word!" he said. "Do you mind frightfully taking a photo of me in front of the sign?"

There was no food in the store. "Is there a restaurant nearby?" she asked the young guy behind the counter. The clerk pointed to a truck-stop type of restaurant almost out of sight down the road.

Darla walked down and when she pushed open the door she noticed immediately that the place was full of men. It was like a Wild West restaurant for truckers. The men all looked scruffy, had stubbled faces, greasy hair, and a bunch of them had sheepskin-type jackets. They all seemed to look up, knives and forks suspended in the air, as she walked to the washroom. Then did the same thing when she came out and took an empty table. What the hell! Had they never seen a hungry, disheveled woman before?

There was an old dolly of a waitress sitting knitting away in the corner. She had a Madame Defarge look about her. Couldn't have given a damn that a customer had arrived. Just kept on knitting. Darla looked at the menu. Pretty good selection. All the usual American breakfast items. Grits and biscuits with gravy. Sausages, bacon and eggs. Stacks of pancakes. She was so hungry she could eat a horse. Madame Defarge still hadn't raised her head. No other waitress around. Darla looked at her watch. She had been waiting for almost fifteen minutes. This was ridiculous and in an odd way, embarrassing. Like there was an unseen prejudice here. What the hell was she sitting here for? Come on, kiddo, just beat it! And, thinking about Michael Jackson, she did a sort of forward moonwalk and, hopefully invisible, she glided out of the place.

She had just enough time before her bus arrived to dash back into the general store. "Beef jerky, please. Yes, a stack of it." And to the clerk's enquiring look: "Hell no ... hold the ammo!"

It was already dark when the bus arrived in Helena, Montana. Darla felt stiff, tired and despondent. She wondered what Charles was doing. Was he missing her, or was he at the university faculty club knocking back drinks? Why should she care? The bus depot was filled with down-on-the-heel people. Maybe they were street people just in there to get warm. It was freezing outside. Some of the guys looked really scary. Like real heroin addicts. All she needed was for someone to snatch her purse. There was an hour and a half wait for her next connection. She killed as much time as she could in the restroom tidying herself up. She looked like hell, like, as her mother would say, she had been pulled through a hedge backwards. She washed her face, tied her hair back, applied fresh makeup, and then went back out to the main area and realized she was feeling so list-less because she hadn't eaten. She lined up and bought a coffee and a ham and cheese sandwich. There was a big, rough, solid-looking guy sitting by himself. *If I go sit next to him everyone will think I'm with him.* Good plan. Two other men from the bus sidled over and sat close by; they were young and both drop dead gorgeous. One had blonde hair that fell over one eye and the other looked South American with olive skin and jet black hair. She had heard them talking on the bus—they were on their way to Phoenix and they were just newly married. Well, hello, in Canada you could do that. She guessed they weren't the only ones feeling a little insecure. She smiled over at them.

After she had wolfed down her sandwich she looked over at the solitary man beside her. "And where are you travelling?"

The big man slowly turned his head. "You talking to me?" His voice was soft and had a deep, rich tone. Dear Lord, he sounded like Sam Elliot. She could listen to that voice forever.

"Yes ... I'm off to L.A. Seems like it's taking forever."

"Know what you mean. I've already arrived, so to speak. I'm waiting for daylight. Here to visit my girl-friend. She's in the hospital."

There was such sadness in this man's eyes. Darla didn't want to press him, but he wanted to talk. His girl-friend had breast cancer. He hadn't seen her in a long while. "I'm feeling kinda anxious about this visit," he said, with such a sweet, gentle smile. He was a Vietnam vet and had kind of dropped out. Lived two miles deep in the woods in a shack a dear aunt had given him.

"What do you do for food?" Darla asked.

"I eat berries. Fish. I kill grouse with a slingshot. I have a small pension." He shrugged and went quiet.

What? Darla stared at his weather-beaten face and his worn out boots. She could feel the brokenness in him and felt overwhelmed. She had a hundred things she wanted to ask him but didn't. And now here it was time to go. She felt like hugging him, but instead touched his arm and left him sitting there.

Next stop, Salt Lake City, Utah. The two young men and another fellow boarded the bus with Darla. The familiar sound of the bus revving up and starting filled the air. Off again into the wild blue yonder. There was starting to be a rhythm with all of this. Bus depots. On and off. New faces. Strange, heart-squeezing stories. There was a huge moon hanging in the sky. The biggest moon Darla had ever seen. Maybe it was the Montana sky that made it look bigger. She leaned against the window and thought of Charles with a heavy heart. They had been perfect for each other in every way. Well, maybe not every way. He could be a cheap bastard at times. Never bought her flowers. And he had the pathetic habit of feeling sorry for himself. Like, he could whine. The silvery moonlight flooded down over the moving landscape. So magical. What a beautiful country, she thought, and fell asleep.

Darla stepped down off the bus in Salt Lake City and took a deep breath. Majestic mountains and a brilliant sunny day greeted her. The air felt so fresh and clean. The two guys called out, "Feel like going for breakfast? We have a couple hours to kill." Bob and Gary had swapped a few stories on the journey. They had been married in a storm of controversy, mainly from Bob's parents. Bob was the blonde. They had endured all the arguments and, as Gary had put it, "Their love had won out." Darla fondly thought of them as "the boys."

"Great idea." She looked over at the other passenger who had joined the bus at Helena. They had discovered his name was Joe. He was a quiet, withdrawn guy, probably around twenty-seven years old, with one of those ugly buzz cuts and a tattoo on his neck.

"Want to join us, Joe?"

He fell in with them, but oddly, at the Howard Johnson's best breakfast buffet ever, said he wasn't hungry and sat silently drinking a coffee and chewing at his thumbnail. He had watchful gray eyes and worn-out jeans. Definitely a strange guy.

Over breakfast, the boys came up with the idea of visiting the famous Mormon temple. A "must see," as they put it. The all trouped to Temple Square and stood blown away at the impressive structure. As they tried the front door a stately, well-dressed man approached them, "May I help you?"

"We'd like to visit your beautiful church, sir." Darla gave him a winning smile. Being Catholic, she had been encouraged to visit any church in the world.

"Only elders may enter," said the Mormon and turned them away.

"Whoa, that's harsh," said Darla

"Hell's bells. What kind of a religion won't let you

into its church?" queried Bob.

"Even Sikh temples welcome the public from all walks of life," grumbled Gary. "They even put food out for the hungry."

What a motley crew they were!

They all climbed back on the bus. At the next lunchtime stop Joe said he wasn't hungry. "I'm going to stay on the bus."

Hello, thought Darla, this kid has no money. When she returned from lunch she dropped a brown bag with a sandwich on his lap. "Can you do me a favour and eat this? I over ordered." The kid ate that tuna fish sandwich like he was going to the chair. Looked like he'd down the brown bag as well.

Next stop, Las Vegas. The boys whispered in Darla's ear that they thought Joe had just been released from prison. Something he was wearing had tipped them off. Darla gave Joe a curious stare, sizing him up. He obviously had no money and he did have a gray pallor like he had a no-sun-for-a-while look, but what the hell? You could say that about everybody in Edmonton!

Finally, the bus pulled into Vegas. "Come on, fellas, let me buy you a goodbye beer?" Darla hated to see the boys go. They were travelling on to Phoenix, a honeymoon of sorts. True to form, Joe said he would rather take a walk around. Darla quietly slipped him twenty bucks.

When the bus took off again, Darla sat looking at

him sitting across the aisle happily eating chocolate bars, chips and pop like a teenager. The boys were probably right about the prison. The $64,000 question being, of course … what time had been paid for what crime?

"I'll look after you until we get to L.A." Joe said with his mouth crammed full with chips, a mess of crumbs littering the front of his shirt.

Really? Methinks a very unlikely bodyguard. He sure as hell was no Kevin Costner. Darla gave him an indulgent wink and a thumbs up and he flashed a goofy smile back.

Now what? The bus driver, instead of settling into his driver's seat, was standing in the aisle to make an announcement. He was looking all puffed up and agitated at the same time.

"The police will be getting on the bus momentarily. Get your I.D. and bus tickets ready."

Darla didn't dare look sideways at Joe. She sensed he was looking straight ahead. In front of her she could see a couple of Mexican-looking people scrambling. *Oh, oh!* Then two plainclothes police entered the bus and started checking everyone's I.D. They told the visibly traumatized Mexicans they were not from Immigration, then they escorted two big, muscle-bound, well-dressed African American males off the bus. The bus erupted, vibrating with buzzed conversations, but the two men were returned just ten minutes later and the bus started off again. Endless miles of ruthless desert. Could anything survive out there? Then, on the horizon in the middle of nowhere, a group of RVs. What the hell were they doing out there? Probably on a list called America's Ten Most Wanted.

Darla was leaning against the bus window like a zombie as they pulled into the Barstow bus depot. Then she sat up straight and gasped. She couldn't believe her eyes. The whole place was full of police cars, barking dogs and cops with guns drawn. *A drug bust? You have got to be kidding!* As soon as the bus pulled into its slot, the police boarded the bus ordering everyone to keep calm and stay sitting in their seats. She could hear a helicopter's propellers whirling above. *Please, dear God, don't start shooting!* It was like being in the middle of a *Die Hard* movie. Oh my heart, Darla thought, it's about to explode. She glanced over at Joe. His fists were clenched, knuckles white. The police hauled the two African American men, now handcuffed, off the bus, and then started searching the luggage in the undercarriage.

As soon as it started, it was over. They had lost their chance to run into the McDonalds that was in full view across from the depot. A blurred image of palm trees blowing in the wind, and the bus was off again and into the endless stretch of desert landscape, the Joshua trees and cactus of the Mojave Desert endlessly flying by. There was a deadly silence. Nobody said one word. Not one word. *I guess*, thought Darla, noting her hands were still trembling, *we're all just relieved we survived the mayhem and are still alive to tell the tale. Death defied in Barstow!* Jesus Mary, did she need a drink! Like, what else could happen? The bus breaking down in the middle of the desert and they would have to drink their own urine?

Finally they pulled into L.A. Darla was so stiff she almost fell off the bus. Oh, thank God, there was Ginette at the other end of the depot! She waved frantically. As she pulled her one piece of luggage along behind her, two scruffy men emerged from nowhere. "Can you give us cigarettes, lady?' One of the men deliberately bumped against her, scaring her half to death. He smelt of garbage and urine. But no! Here came Ginette, advancing on them like a John Deere bulldozer, screaming abuse at the top of her lungs. Darla, however, had reached her breaking point.

"Give them what they want, Ginette!" she screeched in French, bursting into tears. "Give them money, anything, I don't care!" Ginette brushed all that aside. Took Darla's case, pushed one of the guys aside like he was a feather, grabbed Darla and gave her a big hug. "Oh, Ginette," sobbed Darla. "I've had it. My heart and soul can't take anymore!"

"Nonsense, *ma chere.* Blow your nose. The biggest martini is waiting for you. That will fix you up, *n'est-ce pas?"*

ChAPTER 2

I HAD BEEN FRANTICALLY CALLING DARLA for three days when she finally answered her cell.

"Darla? Thank God! I've been worried sick about you. Where are you?"

"Hey, kiddo! Right now I'm in California, sitting in Ginette's house drinking a martini from heaven! Actually, my second martini from heaven."

"Thank goodness! So you're safe and sound. Why the hell haven't you been answering your phone?"

"My phone? Oh, I switched the thing off in Sweetgrass."

"Sweetgrass? Where the hell's that? Never mind. How are you? How are you holding up?"

"Di, I can't tell you! What a trip. I feel I've spent weeks travelling. Actually, it's been 50 hours. There was the biggest moon in Helena ... I wish you could have seen it. The biggest I have ever seen in my life! So much to tell you, kiddo. I've met people you would only meet once in a lifetime. There was this guy who kills grouse with a slingshot."

I could hear Ginette laughing in the background, yelling, "Give them everything they want!" in her thick French Canadian accent.

"Grouse?" I repeated stupidly.

"Yes, to eat. To tell you the truth, Di, at this moment ..." There was a small silence followed by a voice that wobbled. "I'm just grateful and happy to be alive. Look, Di ... Ginette has just started serving dinner. Would you mind if I call you back tomorrow? Okay, kiddo?"

"Okay," I said.

I sat staring at the phone, a little crushed. I had wanted a long chat. She had sounded buzzed. Almost rambling. Talking about slingshots and moons. Not really making sense. Like, what the fuck? I had meant to tell her how much I was missing her and to ask how she was doing emotionally. Ask if she had been talking to Charles.

I slumped back on the couch and sipped on my glass of red wine. Strange. She hadn't even mentioned his name.

CHAPTER 3

LOS ANGELES WAS STARTING TO WEAR DARLA DOWN. It had seemed great at first. It was snowing in Edmonton, raining cats and dogs in Vancouver, and here the weather was gloriously warm. She loved the swaying palm trees, the gentle click-clicking sound they made as the breeze rustled through them. They had fabulous "two for one" happy hours, and everybody welcomed the visitor from the Great White North. Ginette was a rock, but she lived out of the action. You were lost without a car and Darla hated that she was dependent on Ginette. Everything here was fast. Fast food, highway traffic that wasn't only fast it was frantic, like a living death trap, and the people ... everybody here seemed to be in one big perpetual rush. So different from the laid-back pace in Vancouver.

Her sister, Lynn, had phoned urging her to come back home to Montreal. Darla could get a good job there and start over with the support of her family and old friends. It was tempting, but she felt she wasn't quite ready yet, though she'd have to get a job pretty soon. Funds were running low and hello, she didn't have a green card.

Why had she come to L.A.? She couldn't remember the reasoning. She had wanted to run as far away from Charles as she could. And so here she was. No plan A and no plan B. Just a hopeless feeling of being adrift and the pain of knowing Charles was going on with his life. She still wondered what in the hell happened. Still went over every last detail of those last two weeks in Edmonton. How had things gone so wrong?

Now she swore under her breath, "Sweet Jesus, I think I've finally had it." She stared angrily at Amir's retreating back. Ginette was great, but her boyfriend, partner, mate, whatever the hell he was, was giving Darla the creeps of the Hannibal Lector kind. His name was Amir but he looked like a Farouk, one of those shady Egyptian casbah owners with girls for sale in the backroom. He had those heavy-lidded eyes that brought to mind an opium smoker, and a big fleshy nose. What the hell Ginette saw in him was a mystery. Supposedly he was Lebanese and knew Danny Thomas back in the day, *like who didn't*, and every time he was alone with Darla he tried to cop a feel. Like right now. All a big joke, of course, as he grabbed a fistful of her buttocks. Disgusting and gross, but how do you tell a dear friend that her boyfriend is a deviant?

And then there was Ginette's mother, the sweet, long-suffering Mrs. Levesque. She was recovering from her husband's death by knocking back two bottles of red a day and chain-smoking endless packs of Camels.

There were overflowing ashtrays everywhere, fouling up the air with the smell of approaching lung cancer. The husband had now only been dead for three years, but, hello, Mrs Levesque played the grieving widow like she had buried him yesterday.

"Come on out here." Ginette was calling from the seven-by-six-foot deck at the back of the house that she lovingly called the patio. She had switched on the fairy lights that were strung generously around the deck rail and the potted plants and had situated six chairs around a white cane table that sported a flickering, fat red candle. The girls were coming over for a ladies night. Dear old Ginette was trying to cheer Darla up. Mrs. Levesque was already sitting there, her face blurred in a cloud of smoke with an unsteady wine glass in her hand. She was wearing her usual black widow garb but tonight the black blouse had a scooped neckline and behold, she was actually wearing sparkling rhinestone earrings! Things were looking up.

The girls were quite the mixed group, all dressed up in that casual flirty way that made L.A. women look when in the middle of a romantic comedy movie. Rita was probably around thirty, dressed in a flared yellow skirt and an off-the-shoulder white blouse. Pretty in that Latino "flashing dark eye and shy smile" way. Then there was Sylvia. Ginette had gone to school with her back in the old days in Montreal. Sylvia was Jewish.

"Not orthodox," she would say, wagging a finger. "Oh no, none of that bullshit." She was beautifully dressed. Heavy on the jewellery, rings on almost all the fingers, gold around her neck. Like, no lie, if she was tossed into a pool she would sink to the bottom. Then Peggy, who was Irish. Ginette worked with her. She had one of those accents where everything she said sounded like an Irish joke. She was a middle-aged woman with a comfortable persona, you know, the sort that gives you a warm fuzzy feeling. She had four children and her husband had dumped her last year for his blonde, addicted-to-yoga, vegetarian secretary. Amada was the quiet one in the group. A deeply tanned Californian with big blonde hair, gold hoop earrings, and a face that needed help. She was wearing a white silky muumuu-style dress with perfectly manicured crimson red nails and eyebrows that had been plucked to death.

They hadn't even finished their first drink when Sylvia said, "So Darla, I hear you have a broken heart."

That Ginette and her treacherous big mouth. Darla flashed Ginette her favourite death look.

"You could say that. I left town. Unexpectedly."

"Well, darling, there is a big world out there with millions of lonely men." Sylvia gave a knowing smile.

"That's why I invited you girls over," said Ginette, setting down her drink. "Darla, you have to listen. These ladies all joined Match.com and you won't believe what they've been up to."

"Devilment," laughed Rita, tossing her dark hair. It reached halfway down her back. "And fun and nonsense long overdue."

"What the hell is Match?" asked Darla.

"The door to meeting men. Online dating! The best way to meet guys." Amanda's voice was sort of croaky. Like, her larynx needed a lube job like the tin man in the *Wizard of Oz.*

"Online dating? You girls must be crazy ... not for me." Darla raised her eyebrows. "Come on, ladies. Dating strangers through a computer?"

"Well? How do you meet men? In bars? Single dances? This way you talk to the guy online. Get to know him. Go for coffee or a drink, in a public place, whatever, and if you like what you see, you start dating. It's perfect." Sylvia put two fingers on her lips and smacked a kiss into the air.

"Seems so cold and impersonal."

"How can you say that, Darla? You are talking to him and getting to know him comfortably from your own home instead of meeting half-pissed strangers in a bar." That was Peggy jumping in.

"I will never date again." That was Mrs. Levesque's disembodied voice floating on the air.

"Let me tell you a story about the first time I tried it," said Sylvia. "I had been divorced for about a year. It was a pretty lonely time, and I had no idea how to kick start back into dating. Rita finally wore me down and so I joined Match.com. Well, the first week this guy George started chatting to me. He really seemed like a nice guy and so I agreed to meet for coffee. By the time I arrived at the restaurant, I was a bag of nerves. He was an average-looking guy, nice smile and all that, but I couldn't think of a single thing to say to him. My mind just went blank, I was that nervous. Before the latte even arrived I jumped up and said, 'this isn't going to work,' and ran out. But dear old George ran after me, calmed me down, and we started walking. Walking was so much easier than sitting staring at each other. I started to relax. Before long we started laughing. Like, who would have thought two middle-aged people would get on the internet for a date! That sort of thing. From then on it was easy. Then George said, "How about going out for a dinner. We'll do it right. A great restaurant and a bottle of wine." I went home and phoned Ginette right away, I was so excited. 'Get your hair done,' she said, so I did—did my hair, did the manicure, fussed over what to wear and felt like a real woman again. Well, more, I actually I felt like a teenager. It had been a long time since that feeling. I dated George for six months and then he got transferred. That was sad, but I had so much more confidence by then that I went back onto Match.com and started dating again. I've never looked back."

"That's it," said Peggy. "Your confidence is in ribbons when you start. You haven't dated in years and have lost your identity, standing for hours over that bloody kitchen stove. Your husband has run off with some young winsome thing with big boobs and botox and here you are worn out with raising kids and crippled with self-doubt. I tell you."

"Tell about your first time Peggy ... you won't believe this, Darla." Ginette was grinning from ear to ear, busy filling everyone's glass. "Come on," she said as she slopped more wine into Darla's glass, "get into this. It's funny!"

"Oh, faith and the saints, it was a nightmare." Peggy took a long sip of her wine. "The kids were helping me get ready. My daughter was mad, thought I was off my head to be dating at my age. Fuck, I'm fifty-eight! Anyways, I call up Sylvia and tell her I am scared to death and she told me how scared she had been. Just get him talking, she said ... right, Sylvia, remember? ... men love to talk about themselves. So off I go. He's a lovely fellow around fifty something, dressed in a suit and tie, very smart! The dinner comes, steak for him, rack of lamb for me. Then out of nowhere you will not believe what happened. I felt something plop on my lap. I look down and here's the cap of my front tooth, yes, my very front tooth has fallen off and is gleaming in my lap!"

"You have got to be kidding!" Darla started laughing.

"What did you do?"

"I covered it quickly with my napkin, and slipped it into my purse," said Peggy, "and I remembered what Sylvia had said … keep him talking. Talked and talked. I swear I learned everything about that man from kindergarten to his last promotion. I just kept nodding and smiling, with my lips closed, of course, and ate carefully. He booked me a cab to go home so I was off the hook for goodnight kisses or anything naughty like that, so I got away with it. Saw him for a while afterwards. After my tooth was fixed, of course."

"Oh, we all have had such fun with this dating business," Sylvia chimed in. "All of us sitting here have had to start over again. It's not an easy thing to do, start over again, but what are you going to do? Bury yourself in hurt and heartache? It takes a certain kind of bravery to dust yourself down and throw yourself back in the ring. And the guys we have met, they all have stories. Most of them, like us, are lonely and wanting some oomph in their lives."

"We all thought when we got married it was for life. Who thought when we were middle aged and a little over the hill we'd have to start over? We just have to make the best of it." Peggy smiled at Darla. "Don't waste time grieving over a man who isn't worth it, Darla."

Darla looked around the table at the smiling faces and almost felt like crying. They had all suffered the hard knocks of life and here they were cheering her up.

"I just miss my Yvon. No man could ever replace him." Mrs Levesque made the sign of the cross and poured more wine into her glass. She dabbed her eyes with a paper napkin but no one seemed to take any notice. Maybe it had been going on a year or so too long.

"The strangest thing is that you seem to become invisible once you start hitting sixty. Men seem to look right through you," said Sylvia. "Have you found that?"

"I know," said Peggy, "it's like you don't exist. And for God's sake, don't put your real age on Match. com. You know what men are like. They want younger women, so if you put sixty-something for your age only the seventy-year-olds will be answering you. If you say you're eight or nine years younger at least you'll get guys around your own age."

"Talking about old farts, Rita has the craziest story. Well, the funniest." Ginette was busy lighting more candles. She was candle crazy. There was a lineup of them on the railing all sputtering and flickering.

Ginette waved her arms in the air in front of the candles like she was conducting an orchestra. "Atmosphere. We need atmosphere. Come on, Rita ... what do you say? Your turn? Do you want to tell about that night with Bernie?"

"Oh Lord! Does Darla need to hear this? You go ahead and tell it, Ginette ... you tell it best." Rita shook her head, put her hand over her mouth and started laughing.

"Rita works the bar at this luxury Jewish golf club."
Ginette winked at Darla. "Like, imagine the ultimate
hangout for the multi-millionaire crowd. Bernie, this old
fart, keeps telling Rita that she reminds him of his wife
when she was a young beautiful girl. How this can be
when Rita is part Mexican and his wife was 100% Jewish
is a mystery, but ... the wife is dead now and Bernie has
all these fond memories. He's richer than Rockefeller
and the Koch brothers combined and has this lovely
home in Beverly Hills. He says to Rita one night, 'Wanna
come home and watch the ball game with me? I have
the mega big screen. We could knock back a couple of
drinks. What do you say?' Rita is such a softie, she knew
Bernie is so lonely ... anyways, she loves the Dodgers so
she says okay. They get to his house, and she is ushered
up this grand staircase to the entertainment room. The
old guy pours a drink and then says he is going to make
himself more comfortable. She thinks he's looking for
his slippers ..." Ginette starts shaking with laughter.
"Rita ... you have to finish this ... come on, you can tell
it as only you can."

"Alright ... okay ... hold onto your hat, Darla, you
won't believe what the old geezer did next." Rita took
a long gulp of her wine and set her glass on the table.
"Music starts up. Sinatra comes on singing 'Strangers
in the Night.' Bernie enters the room wearing this Drac-

ula-looking black cloak complete with red silk lining, stand-up collar, the whole works, and stands there in the centre of the room. He then dramatically swooshes the cloak apart. He is stark naked with his freaking birthday suit on full display with his skinny, bony little body, and there he is slapping the side of his leg like billy-o and his limp, tiny penis starts to grow. I realize he has one of those pump penis extenders, or whatever the heck they call them, strapped to him. I am frozen in shock, frozen ... it was so unexpected, and Frank is singing *wondering in the night what were the chances* ... then I couldn't help but start to laugh. Almost hysterically. I mean, Bernie must be close to ninety.

"'You little bitch,' he yelled at me, and suddenly it got nasty.

"I grabbed my purse and skedaddled down the stairs. Old Bernie followed me in hot pursuit, yelling and cursing all the way. Talk about a man's hurt feelings! I bolted out the door and it had started pouring with rain. I realized I was running into a dark miserable night with him in hot pursuit and hadn't a clue where I was. I had a sudden burst of inspiration. I reversed, ran back, passing Bernie who by now was really huffing and puffing, and sprinted back into the house and locked the front door. He came up and banged on that door madder than hell. 'Bernie, I am not going to let you in until you apologize. You have been a very rude host, and, by the way, tell me the address here. I'm phoning for a cab.' He was getting soaked out there, hair plastered to his face, and that big ole black cloak was dripping puddles around his bare feet. He gave me his address, but the old geezer didn't apologize until the cab pulled into the driveway. The cabbie never even gave Bernie a second look. I guess they've seen it all in the Beverly Hills."

"What a story!" Darla was holding her sides, swiping the tears from her eyes. "You actually accused him of being a rude host? I would have said 'Bernie you're a fucking pervert.' How did he treat you next time he saw you at the club?"

"Like nothing happened. Those rich guys can't be ashamed. I tell you, though, I heard about Match.com after that and thought whatever happened had to be better than that scene in Bernie's entertainment room, so I gave online dating a try. Have had so much fun since."

Gunter brought out platters of food. Nachos, chicken wings, little empanadas, and a bottle of tequila with shot glasses.

"Are you kidding?" croaked Darla. "Over the top! Looks wonderful."

"Come on, girls, dig in. There are paper plates here and napkins and Coke, lemons and salt if you want to do the tequila crazy thing."

"I'm in," said Peggy, filling a shot glass. "So, girls, here's to romance and sex after sixty." She held the shot glass high for a moment and then knocked the tequila straight back.

"And here's to mega orgasms," said Peggy, neatly downing her tequila in one swift gulp. Darla licked salt off the back of her hand, sucked on a lemon slice and followed suit.

"To orgasms," they all chanted, with even Mrs. Levesque joining in, although she probably didn't know what the word meant since French was her first language.

"So, Amanda, we haven't heard your story yet." Darla gave the woman a questioning look as she munched on a chicken wing.

Amanda smiled coyly. "I've done things a little differently. I'm a Christian, so I have gone for the Christian online dating and I've found pretty decent men. All Christians, of course, and most of them don't drink, which really doesn't bother me. Unlike these wino chicks here, I'm not really into drinking. I'm happy with a glass or two. One or two of the guys have been divorced, but the one I'm dating now seems interested. Mitch has his own business and a lovely home. He's quite a success story."

"That's good," said Darla. "So ... serious, eh? Like, an engagement ring on the horizon?"

"Maybe." Amanda fingered her necklace, clicking the beads with her red manicured nails. "Of course, I would never live with him so it's the altar or zilch."

"You wouldn't live with him?" Darla was incredulous.

"Hell ... she doesn't even give him lovin'. That's the Born Again Christian way!" Ginette laughed.

"Thank God, the Jews don't ask the questions," chuckled Sylvia. "They don't want the answers so they don't ask the questions, and hell, at my age I feel I have to cram in all the loving and living I can get. After twenty years of playing second fiddle to that whoring husband of mine. Ginette, darling, how about a shot of that tequila?"

"Mitch is different," said Amanda. "He is very affectionate and respectful and I appreciate that. We both have given our lives to the Lord Jesus and our church is important to us. Mitch is picking me up later so you'll meet him, Darla."

"What is Mitch doing tonight now that his honey is out with the girls?"

"He's at a firing range. I swear, sometimes he loves guns as much as he loves me."

"Guns? He has a gun?"

"He has a collection of them. Every description. He is proud of his marksmanship and I know you can laugh coming from Canada and all, but I do feel safe with Mitch when I'm out. I know he would protect me at the drop of a hat."

"Like, protect you with his gun? Jesus, Amanda ... If I went out with a guy who was toting a gun I would feel freaked out!" Darla poured another shot of tequila.

"You don't live in L.A., girl. You have no idea what goes on out there."

Mitch showed up and proved to be an ordinary man. A nothing burger. An overweight guy with a tight, unsmiling face and a swagger. Thankfully, he left the guns in the car.

She made up her mind that night after the girls were gone. They were a riot, but she needed to leave L.A. Amir had tried to kiss her on the patio as she was helping clean up the empty glasses. He had been drinking, and his breath stank as he had lurched into her. It was time to go. She was going to take her sister up on her invitation and go back home to Montreal. The city she had grown up in with all the personal history. All those old memories, some good and some pretty bad.

Tennessee Williams had said, *"Time is the longest distance between two places."* Going back to Montreal would be like going back in time, but maybe, who knew, she would find her old self back there.

CHAPTER 4

I HAD BEEN SHOCKED, even dismayed, when Darla had phoned and told me she was going to Montreal. I missed her and wished she'd come back to Vancouver. Life was pretty dull without Darla. But now she was phoning every couple of days full of nonsense and laughter. So much like her old self, it made me smile. She had found a job in accounting at woman's college and found a small furnished apartment in the happening neighbourhood of Le Plateau.

The phone was ringing and talk of the devil, it was Darla calling.

"Di, darling...I need your input. You have to help me write my profile for Match."

"Match?"

"You know...online dating? It's the latest thing. Like, everybody is doing it. Ginette threw a ladies night for me in L.A. and all the women were going crazy for it. I've been thinking I'm ready for lights and action. I've been in Montreal for three months and have yet to go out on a date. I figure this is it. I'm trying online dating. So would you email me a description of myself? Like, what I'm like. I'm stuck. How the hell do I know who I am?"

"I don't mean this unkindly, kiddo, but I don't even know who you are. And I'm one of your best friends."

"Come on, give it a try."

"Well, what do you want me to say? Well-read, loveable kook. Man-eater. Ball buster. Great cook, imaginative storyteller. Does a great Jewish accent and loves Grey Goose?"

"Jesus, Di, I'm supposed to be writing stuff to allure men, not put them off. Look up Match and read some of the profiles. You'll get the drift. Do your best for me. I'm dying to be wined and dined and kissed under the moonlight. Honestly, darling, this is my last kick at the can."

"Okay," I reluctantly agreed. "I'll email you some ideas."

I made one of my favourite sandwiches for lunch, a grilled cheese, red onion, and tomato on rye, cracked open a beer, opened my laptop and started googling. I was gobsmacked by the whole online dating concept. There were so many companies. Plenty of Fish, E Harmony, Match.com, Zoosk, and even sites especially for Christians, like Christian Mingle. The list went on and on. I hadn't realized how big this was. Eighty million people in North America used online dating. That was apparently sixty percent of the single-people pool. Amazing! This was a brilliant way for women to meet men. Tarzan to meet Jane. This was made for Darla.

I would make her profile romantic. Old Hollywood-style romance. Her heading would be "Moon River." And she, of course, was looking for her Huckleberry Finn. The more I wrote, the more I got into it. Darla's finished profile was funny and welcoming. I felt pretty pleased with the email I sent her. I sent her a few pics from last summer when we were sitting on the Sylvia Hotel's patio overlooking English Bay. Darla was showing just the right amount of cleavage and had a terrific tan, and most importantly, we had both just finished the Scarsdale Diet.

CHAPTER 5

DARLA STARED AT HER REFLECTION in the Greyhound bus window. Jeez, was this it? Was a new life about to unfold? She was feeling so hopeful. She had dressed conservatively. Navy blue blazer, white silk blouse. Pearl necklace. Tailored slacks. Franco had done a real number on her hair colour. He had proudly called it an understated pale butter yellow. Nail polish was fresh, Red Hot Rio, like how could you go wrong with a colour named that? The all-important Brazilian had been administered the day before.

She had met up with two other men from Match and knew immediately after half a cup of coffee that they weren't her type. Just no click and no connecting radio waves. The second guy had seemed normal enough before he had blurted out after five minutes of conversation, "I want to be upfront with you. I only have one testicle!" *I mean, spare me.* She had spent the rest of the coffee date steeling herself not to stare at his crotch. A story for one of Ginette's ladies' nights for sure. She went home and deleted his profile and went back on Match and back to the drawing board. It was going to take perseverance to find the right man.

But this Aaron Strong seemed like the real thing. Actually a catch. Well, let's get it straight, maybe the catch of the year. Recently divorced. An architect. Tall, handsome, cultured. They had spoken on the phone for the last three weeks. Now, finally, she was going to meet him. He lived in Vermont. But, hello, Montreal was only an hour and a half away from Vermont. What's an hour and a half when you're in love? He had emailed pics of his house which was more like an estate. Tennis courts. Horses with stables. Like, not on your life was she ever going to climb on top of a horse, but come on, you have to admit horses and stables are impressively sexy. Big huge trees, those beautiful sheltering kind, dotted the grounds.

She started ... her phone was ringing, then smiled. Oh, of course ... it was Di. Who thought it was insane, totally bananas for Darla to be going to meet this guy. Big panic. Darla was crossing the US border. Far from home. Anything could go wrong. Yadda, yadda.

"Hi. I'm on the Greyhound. Everything is fine."

"Promise you will phone as soon as you arrive. Remember to keep your phone on!"

"For Christ's sake, Di. You'd think I was going to meet a psycho serial killer."

"Exactly my point! Who knows who the hell this guy

is. Could be transgender, for all you know."

"You are a riot! Okay, okay. I'll call. Stop worrying!"

If Darla was honest, things hadn't turned out so well in Montreal. She was lonely. Her old friends had scattered, Maria was living in Florida, Ginette in L.A., other friends had scattered. Who knew where they were? And her sister Lynn lived almost two hours away. The women at work were distant. Many were French and she was the only *Anglaise* in her department, and even though she was bilingual she felt very much the outsider. Not one of them had extended an invitation for dinner or an out-of-work activity. That old divide between the English and the French Canadians was still alive and well. She was missing the old gang back in Vancouver. It would be so perfect if this guy Aaron worked out. To have a companion again. She did feel a little nervous. She just didn't want to screw up. Aaron seemed almost too good to be true. Butterflies in her stomach as they passed through customs. The customs officer asked, "Madame, what is the purpose of your trip?"

"A little shopping." She smiled to herself. Oh yeah, good one. Like hello, I'm shopping for a rich, fully-loaded husband.

When she stepped off the bus she didn't see him right away. The usual scruffy crowd that loiters around bus stations screened her view and then, there he was. Dressed impeccably in a dark suit. Maroon-striped tie.

Tall. Full head of dark hair. Beautiful warm brown eyes. He thrust out his hand. Firm handshake.

"So pleased to meet you, Darla." Very formal. "I thought we would have dinner in town and if you are up for it afterwards, I would like to show you my home. There is a great Italian restaurant or a steak house, which would you prefer?

"Let's do Italian."

He took her arm as they walked to the restaurant a short block away. Very festive, linen tablecloths, candles ... delightful. Once they were seated, he cleared his throat and said, "I don't drink, but I invite you to have a glass of wine if you so wish." *He doesn't drink.* Her throat was aching for a cool glass of Chardonnay.

"I'd love a glass. Thanks."

The waiter, a good-looking Italian kid, the type with those dancing dark eyes, brought the menu over. "Good evening, folks. My name is Lorenzo. What can I get you to start?"

She resisted the impulse to say "make the wine half a carafe" as Aaron ordered two pasta specials.

"Well, this is lovely. I finally get to meet you and here we are!" she said.

"I'm a little rusty with the dating game," he said, somewhat shyly. "Why don't you tell me about yourself?"

Darla took a deep breath. She was good at this.

Drawing people out. "Well, you read my profile, so you know quite a bit about me. What I loved about your profile was your interest in American history. George Washington, Thomas Jefferson ... interesting times in American history. I have actually visited both their homes." It was odd; the whole time she had been talking, he hadn't made eye contact. Had sort of been looking behind her, like over her head. She fought the compulsion to turn and see who or what he was staring at.

Lorenzo arrived with the wine and it seemed only minutes until he was delivering their seafood pasta. "That is some fast service." She smiled.

"Well, it is the special. Already prepared, Madame." The cheeky little devil gave her a wink as he sprinkled the parmesan. She half wished he was her date.

Aaron looked across the table once the waiter left and said very formally, "I'd like to say a prayer." Without further ado he reached over the table and held her hands in his. "Dear Lord, thank you for this lovely meal and thank you for bringing Darla safely to this table."

Are you kidding?

When she opened her eyes he was smiling at her. Was it a joke? She wasn't sure. She flashed him her warmest smile and leaned a little forward to showcase the cleavage. Her wine glass was sadly empty. To hell with it! She beckoned the waiter over. Aaron watched with a stiff smile as Lorenzo poured the wine.

"My father was Welsh," he said, forking his fettuccini around on his spoon. "He was a minister. Methodist. Quite a religious man. He convinced my brother and I to sign a temperance contract abstaining for life from alcohol, and from sexual relations until we were married."

Darla choked, and her shoulders began to spasm. No use, her wine spluttered all over the table. And, of course, while he was talking in that monotone voice he was staring over her head again … at what? At least she had time to hastily mop the wine up with her napkin before he seemed to notice.

"So," Darla said, in a shattered voice, "alcohol has never touched your lips?"

"Never. Abstinence has been a way of life." *What a simply joyous, bloody great start to the evening.*

Before they left the restaurant she excused herself to freshen up in the washroom. As she stood in front of the mirror she gave a gasp of horror. The two top buttons on her silk blouse had become undone. Her ample breasts jutted out in all their glory like magnificent bow figure-heads on a tall sailing ship. No wonder the poor man kept looking straight over her shoulder. Why hadn't he mentioned it? He was either very shy or terribly inhibit-ed. Either one brewed for a rocky night ahead.

As they went to get into his car he stopped and faced her, smiling. "I want you to meet someone special in my life." He thrust open the back car door and the most massive black German Shepherd known to man sprang out from the back seat. "Meet Caesar!" he cried joyfully.

Darla jumped backwards, which was really almost an impossible physical act for someone pushing sixty in three-inch high heels, and almost fainted. She was terrified of big dogs, never mind a monstrous, ugly brute like this. She managed to whisper, "Hi, Caesar," as she squeezed into the car.

She felt paralyzed with fear as they drove to his house as the dog kept sniffing the back of her neck. She hoped to God he wasn't slobbering saliva into Franco's understated pale butter yellow. They sped through endless winding country roads. The sun was setting and long dark shadows fingered the meadows. It was the most beautiful countryside but she was filled with an apprehensive, uneasy feeling. Di's words kept ringing in her ears. It was true she really didn't know a damn thing about Aaron except right now she had learned about his alcohol abstinence and that he had a brute for a pet. And ... hold onto your hat ... he hadn't had sex until he was married. If she was truthful, she took chances, this being one of them, but, she reassured herself, during their fairly long telephone chats he had come across as the pillar of society. She could hear Di saying, *"Oh yeah, a pillar!"* They went through a picturesque covered wooden bridge that led straight onto his property. There were the tennis courts and over there under some shady trees, the horse stables.

So he was the real deal. Maybe there was hope yet.

The house was magnificent. Huge glass windows. The view spectacular over lawns leading to wooded slopes. But they were in the middle of nowhere. She wondered if her cell phone would work from here. Thank the Lord, Caesar had been put outside in a huge dog pen. Aaron had seated her in a room with a high timbered ceiling, a huge stone fireplace and beautiful teal leather couches. He had gone to make tea. *Tea!* No such thing as a bar in this house but this house was made for entertaining. She imagined ushering guests into this beautiful living room. Saying to her guests, "Dinner will be served soon. Make yourselves at home." Of course, she would be serving pre-dinner martinis. Maybe they could afford a butler for functions.

Two of the walls were fitted with wooden oak bookshelves filled with books, hundreds of books it seemed. Quite the library. You could tell a lot about a person from the books they read. She sauntered over and felt pure delight as she read the titles. So many were her favourites. So she and Aaron did have a lot in common after all. Steinbeck, Hemingway, Tennessee Williams. As Aaron came in balancing a tea tray, she smiled warmly at him, waving Capote's *In Cold Blood* in the air. "Oh, I love your collection. It is so great to meet another lover of books!" It seemed to soften him up a little. Lessen the tension between them. They sat and drank tea and actually had a good time yakking away about Kerouac, had the world arrived at George Orwell's 1984. They both loved the weirdness of Tom Robbins. They jumped from book to book like they were on a book safari. It was odd, though, that he had chosen to sit on a separate couch away from her. He told her a little about his brother, Lionel. He was the one who had encouraged Aaron to go on Match. Lionel, who was younger, was an accountant. Aaron had gone to Yale. Lionel had gone to Columbia. A little sibling rivalry creeping in here? Lionel was also in the throes of wrapping up a divorce. Boy, these Strong brothers were leading parallel lives.

"Is that the two of you over there?" Darla asked, pointing at a photo sitting on the bureau of two men in tennis whites.

"Yup, taken here, outside on the courts."

Hmm. Tall, dark, and handsome. Lionel was a hunk of burning love.

Then the conversation changed into what his married life had been like. No children. Stories about his wife. She was an insufferable woman. Wealthy, spoiled. And the most heartbreaking thing she was doing now, after all the other awful stuff, he told her, was that she was fighting him for custody of Caesar.

"Caesar... *the dog*?" Darla stared at him in disbelief.

"Of course, Caesar my dog," Aaron snapped. "Did you think I meant Caesar the Roman Emperor?"

"It's just I've never heard of court battles over dogs ... it's usually a dogfight over the kids ..." Her voice faltered. *Was it clever or stupid, how she had chosen the word dogfight?*

Aaron stood abruptly, announcing, "Well, you've had a long day. Let me show you to your room."

To her room?

She followed Aaron up the wide staircase. It was a lovely little room. The bedside lamp had already been turned on. The bed sheets were folded back in the welcome position. Her small overnight bag was resting on a wicker chair. When had he done all this? Then with a stiff smile he said, "I hope you have a comfortable night," and turned on his heels and left.

She lay in bed in the carefully selected black negligee from La Vie en Rose, staring at the ceiling. What the hell had the whole evening been about? Maybe he was going to knock on her door and ask to come in. She felt uneasy. Not about that, him knocking on the door, but where was that monstrous, bloody German Shepard? Did Aaron let him in at night? In all probability the man was curled up in bed with the brute right now. She texted a brief message to Di saying "all is well." What a joke. She felt lonely and lost; here she was in the wilds of Vermont. Had she said something wrong? Was it because she had had two glasses of wine in the restaurant? Here she thought she was going to have the most romantic night of her life and she hadn't even been kissed. There was a difference between being a gentleman and this. There was obviously something wrong with the guy. He was so uptight and closed up like a sealed submarine. Yet obviously lonely or he wouldn't be on Match. Maybe his Methodist father had done a number on him when he and his brother were kids. Making them sign abstinence contracts! So many people had unseen wounds.

Well, she thought with a weak smile, *things had not worked out.* But, like Scarlett O'Hara … she had to remember that tomorrow was a brand new day. She propped herself up on the down-filled pillows analyzing the night's conversation one more time. Watery moonlight filtered through the louvered blinds and rested on her pearls. Her mother's pearls were the one thing of value her mum had left her. That song … what was it? "Moonlight in Vermont"? She hummed a few wistful bars. Maybe kiddo, you just should have held back on the word *dog-fight!* Or maybe you shouldn't have flashed your boobs in the restaurant. Oh my God, hells bells, how did these things happen? What a comedy routine. Wait until she told Di. When she eventually fell asleep, she had a grin on her face.

The knocking on the door woke her up. Morning sun was streaming into the room. "Hello," she croaked.

"If you're ready for some tea I'll bring some up in a few minutes."

She jumped up and raced into the adjoining ensuite. Splashed water on her face, quickly cleaned her teeth, gargled with mouthwash and brushed her hair. Just a little soft pink lipstick. She pumped the pillows furiously and jumped back into bed, feigning a sleepy just-woke-up look, lounging back just in time as he came in. Aaron looked as fresh as a daisy. Showered and shaved and dressed in an immaculate long-sleeved baby blue shirt and khakis. He carefully set the tea tray on the bed then stared at her and smiled. *What ... he was making eye contact?*

"How was your night?"

"Oh, lovely. Such a comfy bed. And it's so peaceful here. I thought I was in a National Park." She had only sipped on the tea for a minute when he took away the tray, set it on the dresser and sat on the bed. She regarded him cautiously. *What now?* He had a very intense look.

She stared, mesmerized, at his hand as it slid under the bed sheets. He was actually staring deeply into her eyes. Now his breathing became erratic as his fingers discovered the Brazilian. Dear God! He hadn't even kissed her! "Aaron, what the hell! Just hold on a moment here." She struggled to find a place to set her half-full cup of tea. He grabbed her free hand and placed it on his crotch. There was a lot of muscle-growing action going on down there. "Aaron!" her voice was a strangled gasp. "Like, slow down ..."

Out of the corner of her eye she saw something dark move. Then a growl like the wildlife of Africa on the attack. There was Caesar, baring his teeth, hackles raised and a deep feral growl emitting from his throat like foghorn on a stormy night. Darla screamed. At the top of her lungs. She flew out of the bed, and the teacup was tossed as she dashed into the ensuite, locking the door.

"I'll take you to the bus station now," Aaron said when she finally ventured down the stairs fully clothed.

She was delivered not to the convenient bus station closest to the Canadian border, but to the closest one to his house. It was a long bus ride back. A deeply contemplative one. She wondered what Ginette's gang would think of this, her first real online date. "Dust yourself down, jump back into the ring ..." Wasn't that what they had said? And it was then she realized with glee the first thing she was going to do when she arrived back in Montreal.

"Have you anything to declare?" asked the Canadian customs officer at the border.

Darla, guessing an insane experience wouldn't be an acceptable answer, replied, "Not this time, Officer. Couldn't find what I was looking for."

chapter 6

IT TOOK NO TIME AT ALL for Darla to find brother Lionel on Match. She sent him a carefully crafted email. After all, she knew more or less exactly what the guy was like.

Dear Man in Motion,

I read your profile and would love to hear from you. I am looking for a companion who has high morals and ethics but also knows how to enjoy the finer things in life. I see you have a lovely German Shepherd dog. I am a great lover of dogs but unfortunately am not allowed to have pets at my residence. I hope you read my profile and we can meet for coffee soon.

Regards,
Moon River

The next day an email from Lionel arrived.

Dear Moon River,

What a lovely surprise to hear from you. Loved your profile. I will be in Montreal on business next week. Where would you like to meet?

Regards,
Man in Motion

Darla called Ginette in Los Angeles and told her what she was doing with the Stone brothers. "Tell the girls," she said. "I want them to know I am being a devil and enjoying every moment of it."

"But what if they find out ... these Stone brothers? What if they get mad?"

"Oh, Ginette, don't worry. One lives in Vermont and one lives in New Hampshire. I'm hoping they will find out. Rattle up their dull lives and give their Methodist asses a shake-up."

"Just remember, *ma cherie*, Americans have guns!"

In the end it was Lionel who chose Gibbys, a restaurant in old Montreal with lots of atmosphere. Wooden beams with the original old stone walls and intimate lighting. It had been horse stables in the old days but now was renowned as one of Montreal's finest. When Lionel walked in, she recognized him immediately. He was what you would call a fine figure of a man. He stood for a moment and surveyed the room, and when he saw her, his face lit up with a brilliant smile. He was wearing a fur hat, Dr. Zhivago style, dramatic as hell, and a light sprinkling of snow covered the shoulders of his fashionable long black coat. She felt her heart skip a beat. Holy smokes! *This was Lionel?* He checked in his coat and hat and strode across the room.

"Well, *hello*, Moon River!" He extended his hand.

She felt like jumping up and hugging him, but politely shook hands. She couldn't stop smiling at him and those lovely, blue crinkly, dancing eyes kept smiling back. He had beautiful dark cropped hair that was shot with silver. He was wearing an elegant dark suit with a light blue shirt. Top button undone. No tie.

"Sorry I'm a little late, ran into a troop from the Cirque du Soleil and they directed me here. Weather is nasty. Let's order some wine," he said picking up the menu. "Let's get the show on the road and I'll tell you all about it."

Hallelujah! This was no Aaron Stone sitting here. Amazing and so wonderful how brothers could be so different.

When the second glass of wine was poured, Darla went to the washroom. Not necessarily to freshen up, but to get ahold of her feelings. She stared long and hard at herself in the mirror. She was dressed in an elegant jersey-knit black dress adorned, of course, with Ma's pearls. Her hair was pulled back and piled up and Franco's blonde buttercup colour was still holding up. She had to admit she looked pretty good, but it was her heart that was in trouble. Something was happening and it was unnerving. Lionel had such sensuous lips. He smiled at her and she felt goosebumps all over. *Like, what the …?* The conversation between them was flowing like magic. He was funny, but she was also making him laugh and when he laughed, he threw back his head and this lovely, rumbling endearing belly laugh filled the air. They devoured the special Gibbys' pickles and French loaf and they both ordered the same meal. Medium-rare ribeyes, house salad and Gibbys' special Monte Carlo double-baked potatoes. When he had listened to her giving the identical order to the waiter that he was about to order, he had raised his eyebrows and stared into her eyes and said, "Hmmm … we might be in trouble here!" Plus, he was knocking back the wine like it was an old friend. How was it all going to end?

He mentioned his father once, and she had almost said, "Oh, that old mean-spirited son of a bitch." That had been a little cause for concern … like, hello, she was momentarily shaken to the core. He hadn't talked about Aaron yet. She was waiting. "Remember, and don't forget," she told her flushed image in the washroom mirror, "this date is all about, and only about, playing a joke on Aaron!" She gave a big sigh, refreshed her vibrant Russian Red lipstick, and went back to the table.

Lionel was saying goodbye to someone on the phone. "My brother," he explained, closing his phone and smiling at her. "We're driving down to Florida to visit my dad next week. It's his eighty-sixth birthday."

She sat down on her chair with a plop and stared at him, stricken. *Aaron!*

She swallowed hard and willed her voice to sound normal. "You have a brother?"

"Just one. Two years older, pretty smart guy. Oh, here comes dinner."

There was a companionable silence as they ate. The ribeyes were a dream. "I'll have to get the recipe for these Monte Carlo potatoes," she said. "They're amazing."

"Your wish is my command. I'll get it. Even if I have to torture the cook." He pushed his plate gently to one side. "So, okay," he said, leaning back in his chair and swirling his wine glass. "Question time. Three of your top-ten books."

"Hmmm ... let's see. *Moby Dick, Love in the Time of Cholera* ... oh, I have so many favourites, but I guess *Wuthering Heights*."

"I'm impressed. You must be a big reader. Every one of those is a good read."

"That I am. Okay, how about you?"

"*Heart of Darkness, In Cold Blood*, the Sherlock Holmes series."

"*Lionel.* Three of *my* favourites! But it's not fair. You

were prepared for that question."

"Moving along, question number two … most bizarre job interview."

She laughed out loud. "Do you do this to all your dates? Interrogate them?"

"What? *Interrogate?* No. No. No. No. You mean do I ask questions? I thought it would be a good way to get to know you. You know … instead of talking about the weather."

"Okay. Crazy job interview. I do have a good one. I was desperate for a job at the time, otherwise I wouldn't have even bothered, but behold, in the want ads—a job for a bookkeeper for a pet cemetery."

"A pet cemetery?" He leaned back in his chair, smiling in anticipation.

"So off I go dressed to the nines, right on time for the interview. The office is your normal-looking office setup, except it has wallpaper with this bizarre cat and dog pattern. The guy interviewing me, Roger, seemed like your regular guy. All was going well and then he said, 'Now we do ask the person holding this position to participate in our pet burial services. It's sort of out of the realm of the regular bookkeeping duties. How do you feel about that?'

"'I'm sure that would be fine,' I said smartly. 'What would you expect me to do?'

"'Let me walk you through the process,' he says. He

takes me on a tour of this little church. It had pews and
stained-glass windows, just like your normal church.
He leads me to a little closet and pulls out a black robe.
'Slip this on and follow me.' We walk outside and there
behind the office building is a pet cemetery. Lots of little
crosses and headstones. We stand by one of the graves
and he hands me a sheet of paper and a big honking bible
and asks me to read. I start to read off the sheet of paper,
just a little self-conscious that my black robe is blowing
majestically in the breeze and I look like a freaking Elmer
Gantry nutter. I mean, there is traffic driving by. 'We
are gathered here today to say our last goodbye to our
beloved Rufus ... ' I stop reading and stare at Roger. 'You
want *me* to read pet eulogies like I'm a Minister of the
Cloth?'

"'Are you okay with it? You sound great, by the way.'

"I started laughing. I couldn't help it. I said, 'Roger,
how the hell can you possibly keep a straight face spouting this kind of a spiel?' I almost said, *spouting this shit.*
I think it was at that particular moment that I fouled up
the winning interview."

Lionel was laughing so hard he was wiping away
tears with his napkin. "Priceless. Oh my God. Pet eulogies. What a way to make a buck."

"'Priceless' being the key word. Believe me, there's
big money in it. Uh oh. I think we're laughing too loud.
People are staring at us."

"So what. Let them stare. They're thinking, 'Look at that lucky guy having so much fun with that beautiful blonde.' They can eat their hearts out."

"Oh, really. Beautiful blonde? I can handle that." She smiled at him across the table. "Okay. Back on track, then. Your turn. Favourite childhood holiday?"

"That's easy. Going back to Wales. My grandparents were Welsh. Castles everywhere. These wild beaches that stretched for miles. Cliffs and mysterious caves. You know, the kind that smugglers would have used. They had donkey rides on the beach, no kidding, and these 'donkey men,' I don't know what else to call them, would run like the wind beside us holding the reins. A hell of a job. Talk about a rough way to make a buck, never mind pet eulogies. And there was this place called Barry Island that had a wonderful funfair with the most terrifying roller coaster you could dream up."

"One of my best friends is Welsh. Diane R for Rhonda Foley. How Welsh is that! She lives in English Bay, Vancouver. Actually, I used to live right around the corner from her. She's mad about Tom Jones."

"Tom Jones, eh? Well get this. My uncle lived on the same street in Port Talbot as Richard Burton. How's that for uanship? Burton was called Richard Jenkins then."

"You showoff!"

"Oh, yes! My Uncle Jimmy and Ritchie Jenkins were just like this." He held up his hand and wiggled two crossed fingers. That wonderful laugh again.

"You're putting me on!"

"Uh uh … like this!" He wiggled his fingers again and blew her a kiss across the table.

All she could do was to helplessly laugh. How could two brothers be so different? Maybe their mother had "lovers."

"FYI, you have a little Richard Burton-y in the way you talk yourself."

"I do?"

"Yes. You know. That deep voice, all passionate and full of emotion."

"Whoa … you're going to make me blush."

Those blue eyes. Blue and deep as the Aegean Sea, caressing her, causing a flood of forbidden thoughts.

"Oh, I'll make you blush, all right!" she said, without thinking.

"I bet you can," he said softly, "and I hope you will." There was brimming humour in his eyes.

Darla thought, *what the hell did I just say?* And to her horror, she felt a hot blush staining her cheeks.

The waiter saved the moment. "Would Madame or Monsieur care for dessert?"

"Are you going to order the same thing as me again?" he asked.

She said brightly, "I don't have to look at the menu I know what I want." *Oh yes, do I know what I want. For*

God's sakes, Darla, pull yourself together. Remember. This evening is nothing more than a practical joke!

When the waiter brought two crème brûlée to the table, Lionel reached over and held her hands. They were strong, beautifully manicured hands and an electric current flowed like hot lava through them into her fingers. She felt her nipples stiffen under the soft fabric of her dress.

"I bet this is just the tip of the iceberg," he said in a low voice. "It's like ..." he half-crooned the lines to the song, *'when you get caught between the Moon and New York City.'* I'm willing to bet you love martinis with olives, shaken not stirred, and South Pacific islands and reading in bed with the rain pounding outside ..."

"And Wimbledon tennis, and the sound of Big Ben and ..."

"Broadway musicals and black and white movies like *Casablanca* and ..."

"The *Treasure of the Sierra Madre* ..." she felt breathless. Was it the wine making them crazy? They held hands, just staring at one another. There was a silence; the only sound Darla could hear was the clamouring of her heart. It was hammering in her chest.

"What do you say we down these crème brûlées and get the hell out of here?" Lionel had a serious look as he signaled the waitress over. *"Excusez-moi, l'addition, s'il vous plait."*

The wind was gusting in sheets off the St. Lawrence River, blowing the driving snow right into their path as they walked down the cobbled street of Place d'Youville. Lionel had placed a supportive arm firmly around her waist.

"Let's get this cab," shouted Lionel above the wind. *"Auberge Bonaparte, s'il vous plait,"* he told the cabbie as they clambered in. "I thought foolishly we could walk. Who would have thought the weather would go crazy on us like this?"

"Montreal? You're kidding. *Tabarnak,*" said the cab driver. "The fucking snow, she never stop."

She didn't ask him why they were going to his hotel. She knew.

They stood for a moment in his room. It was beautifully furnished. Polished wooden floors, two tasteful lamps with low lights, and in the shadows a king-size bed with huge white down pillows. Lionel took off his coat, shook off the snow and hung it up and then took off Darla's coat and did the same. They stood silently, staring at each other. Then Lionel took off his jacket and they kissed and embraced like the heavens were opening up. Darla took off her winter scarf and watched him as he undid the buttons on his shirt and then let the shirt slide onto the floor. His body was muscular and toned and still lightly tanned from last year's summer. Her knees felt weak. There was a small intake of breath from him as she unzipped her dress and let it fall to the floor. He never took his eyes off her as he unzipped his pants and stepped out, leaving them to fall. She slid off her pantyhose, took a deep breath and he unhooked her lace bra and tossed it on the floor, then pulled off her lace panties. There was a lump in her throat. She had never felt so vulnerable and dizzy. He crossed over to her and pulled her gently into his arms. Her flesh felt like it was melting. He kissed her face and then her lips. She let out a moan as his hands grasped her bare buttocks and pulled her hard against him. "I swear I hear music," he said, and carried her to the bed.

Afterwards, as she lay nestled against his sleeping body, she thought of many things. Her head still in the clouds, she felt a happiness she hadn't in years, if ever. How could this have happened? Why hadn't she stuck to her practical joke plan? The truth was, she had found him totally irresistible. She had been struck by lightning and now there were dues that would have to be paid. What was going to unfold when he told Aaron about the amazing Canadian girl, Moon River, that he had met on Match.com? What would her beautiful Lionel think of her? She had met the man of her dreams, and in one stroke of cruel fate had lost him before their love story had even begun.

ChapTER 7

SHE ARRIVED BACK AT HER APARTMENT AT FIVE A.M. She had slid out of bed carefully, not wanting to wake Lionel, quietly dressed, and then called a cab from the hotel foyer. Nothing made you feel more shame than taking a cab home from a hotel before dawn's early light when you're still wearing last night's clothes. She didn't immediately notice her answering machine light flashing on the kitchen counter. It was a message from Maria in Florida. Maria was one of her dearest and oldest friends. They had grown up together in the old Montreal French-Canadian neighborhood of Montreal North. It was a given, playing with all the French kids on the street, that Darla had learned to speak French. In those days no-one had any money. Most of the neighbourhood's fathers had returned from World War II damaged beyond repair. Darla's father, who had served in the Royal Canadian Air Force as a fighter pilot, was not happy unless he had a drink in his hand. Maria's dad, who like many French Canadians had been a conscientious objector, had a hair-trigger temper and couldn't hold down a job. The girls' unspoken empathy of each other's home situation led them to bond easily. Let's face it. There was no such thing as normal after the war. The whole world was trying to recover from the devastation. So the girls found a way to make the best of things and together they laughed their way through the meager pickings of their childhoods.

Maria's familiar thick French accent was distraught. "Darla, call me. My beautiful Jean-Pierre has gone—*il est mort.*" Darla was aghast! Jean-Pierre, Maria's husband, had died of a heart attack. Bang. All over, just like that. He was only fifty-nine. The funeral was to be held on Friday, in three-days time. Please, Maria asked, was it possible for Darla to come down to Florida? She needed her best friend by her side.

Darla sat on the edge of her bed, still holding the phone. Of course she would fly down. She wouldn't let Maria down. She desperately needed coffee. She needed to think. Darla filled the coffee pot and jumped into a long hot shower. She would phone the office to let them know she would be gone for a few days. That was easy. Then what about Lionel? What to do? She shook her head. He didn't have her phone number or address. They had communicated solely through Match.com. The best thing to do was to let the whole screwed-up, agonizing affair have a natural death. She would close down her

Moon River account with Match.com ... or maybe she could just block him, and then he wouldn't be able to contact her. She was on the verge of tears. She felt the lowest of the low; sometimes life was such a bitch. After her shower Darla booked her flight to West Palm Beach, but her heart felt torn.

She would have to think about Lionel tomorrow.

Darla went directly to the Buccaneer Pub. She could see Maria sitting on a bar stool talking away to Bobby. She was a large-boned woman with a face that one could say was the map of a hundred disasters. She was dressed in a powder-blue suit with a small, ridiculous black velvet hat perched on her head. The hat had a cloud of fine black feathers and a tiny black netted veil. As she talked the feathers puffed softly up and down. Bobby had been working behind that bar for at least ten years, he knew everybody who was anybody in Palm Beach Shores and he was particularly fond of Maria. He had helped her through some tough times when Jean-Pierre used to binge drink.

"Hey, Darla! What a surprise!" He smiled as Darla sat down. She had met Bobby two years ago when she had escaped a particularly rainy Vancouver winter and had vacationed here in West Palm Beach with Maria for three weeks.

"I was just ordering rum and coke. For Jean-Pierre

and me. You having one, Darla?" Maria swiveled on the stool to face her, opening up her arms and hugging Darla. Her voice, with its strong French accent, was like gravel. She was a sturdily built woman with dark blue eyes. Her face was rescued by a redeeming smile that could light up a room. She had worked hard as a bartender all of her life, and had the varicose veins and rough hands to prove it. Darla was fond of saying, "What do I think of Maria? Maria is bigger than life!"

"Sure." Darla nodded her head uneasily. She was dreading this afternoon; it was going to be a nightmare, but for Maria's sake she would see it through.

"So where's our Jean-Pierre?" asked Bobby, setting up the drinks on the bar. "Is he in the gents?"

"Jean-Pierre's gone. I was just about to tell you, Bobby." Maria dabbed her red-rimmed eyes with a clump of damp Kleenex. "He went last week."

Bobby stopped, a glass in mid-air. "What do you mean he's gone? Don't tell me you guys broke up."

"Jesus no, Bobby! Why would you think that? We loved each other. My Jean-Pierre, he died." She burst into tears. "Oh God, I miss that man so much. The pain!" She thumped her chest.

Bobby put the last drink on the counter, looking confused. "But you said a drink for Jean-Pierre?"

"Yes! Yes! In his honour. I will bury him today. I am going to bury him at sea. Darla is going to help me with the ceremony. Now get yourself a drink, Bobby. We are going to toast to my one and only love. *L' homme de mes reves.*"

Bobby poured a shot of whiskey, looking very solemn. "I can't believe this," he muttered. "Jean-Pierre was only in here a couple of weeks ago, healthy as a horse."

"To Jean-Pierre, *mon mari, mon amour.*" Maria held the glass high then knocked the drink back. Darla and Bobby murmured, "To Jean-Pierre," and followed suit.

"Another round," ordered Maria. "I am going to send this man I loved off with a wonderful goodbye. I am going to honour his wishes. He always wanted to be buried at sea. You know, Darla ... you heard him say that."

"I heard him," said Darla.

Bobby coughed delicately. "Hmmm ... another one for Jean-Pierre?"

"For Christ's sakes Bobby ... pour it! For Jean-Pierre! He's here." She rapped her fingers on a white cardboard shoebox that was sitting on the bar, and pushed it closer to Bobby's side of the counter for him to see.

Bobby stood stock still. Darla looked down at her feet.

"Jean-Pierre's in there?" Bobby's voice was a little on the husky side.

"Yes, he's here with me! I told you that, Bobby. I'm burying him today. That's why I brought him here."

Bobby coughed and cleared his throat then set the drinks on the counter. Darla was about to take her drink, but Maria raised her hand. "Hold on!" She struggled to her feet and held her glass high. "To the most wonderful man in the whole world, my Jean-Pierre!"

"To Jean-Pierre!" Bobby and Darla chanted.

"Where are you burying him at sea?" asked Bobby. "That's a tall order!"

"Out 'ere in the bay. I have bought tickets on the *Shamrock* ... the 2:00 pm sailing."

"The *Shamrock*?" Bobby gaped at her.

The *Shamrock* was the vessel of choice for many tourists seeking the ultimate sightseeing and fishing expedition. It held approximately fifty passengers, who were provided with fishing lines, bait and unlimited quantities of liquor.

"Well, what the fuck am I supposed to do?" wailed Maria. "I promised him a burial at sea. I can only do the best I can do. Darla will help me, and I know it will all turn out to be beautiful. A proper send-off like I promised him." Tears streamed down her face. She dabbed the clumped up Kleenex to her eyes, took one of Jean-Pierre's rum and cokes and downed it.

Bobby came around to their side of the bar and put his arms around both of them. He kissed the top of their heads. "The best of luck, Maria! You are making Jean-Pierre proud."

Darla wasn't sure how this was going to work out. Maria was sitting on a bench on the top deck of the

Shamrock clutching the cardboard shoebox on her lap. A plastic bag laying by her feet enclosed a twenty-six ounce bottle of Captain Morgan rum. Jean-Pierre's favourite brand. The very one that had encouraged him to become an alcoholic.

"We have to wait until we are out to sea." Maria was rocking slightly back and forth.

"How far out?" asked Darla, making it sound like a casual question.

"Far out," said Maria, looking at the receding coastline. "I will know when it's the time."

The boisterous holiday crowd around them were having a great afternoon. They were dressed in shorts and sandals, sunscreen slapped on their faces. Casting fishing lines and getting pleasantly buzzed on the free booze. There was a pleasant smell in the air of frying onions and chili dogs. Little kids chased each other around, screaming as they ran. Too bad they didn't know they would be attending a funeral any moment now.

Maria suddenly straightened up, alert. The captain, smartly dressed in a crisp white uniform adorned with gold buttons and epaulets, was walking briskly towards a small podium. Darla heard someone murmur something about a dolphin-sighting announcement. Maria swiftly pulled down the little veil on her hat, and fast as a gazelle she darted across the deck with Jean-Pierre and the Captain Morgan bag under her arm.

As the captain detached the mic from its holder, she grabbed his arm. "Captain, I am on a mission. I am going to bury my husband at sea, and I want you and all the passengers to join me in the ceremony." She snatched the microphone from the stupefied captain and bellowed into the mic in her thick French Canadian accent, "Please! Fellow passengers, drop your fishing rods, put down your drinks and join hands. I am going to bury my dear husband, Jean-Pierre, here at sea, and I want you to join with me in The Lord's prayer." She started reciting the words. "Our Father who art in heaven, hallowed be Thy name, Thy Kingdom come …"

Darla looked around. No one was going to understand what the hell was going on. Not with that accent butchering every bloody word. But slowly the noise subsided. People began to awkwardly hold hands. A big-bellied guy wearing a T-shirt emblazoned with "Don't Mess with Texas" standing behind her said, "What the fuck is going on?"

"Shush," a voice said reverently. "A funeral."

When Maria had finished the prayer, she held up the shoebox. "Now goodbye to my dear Jean-Pierre, the best husband in the world. I now commit your soul to the deep and to the arms of Jesus Christ our Saviour. Amen!" She threw the shoebox into the ocean and blew kisses as it hit the waves and sank. Then she pulled the bottle of Captain Morgan rum out of the plastic bag and hurled it after the box. There was a satisfying splash.

There was a moment's silence as the crowd on the deck seemed unsure of what to do, and then a tremendous applause and clapping filled the air. A few people waved goodbye.

"That went well," said Darla, handing Maria a double rum. "You really pulled it off. I don't know why I was so worried."

Maria took the drink, a happy smile on her tear-stained face, and leaned, emotionally drained, against the deck rail. Her blue mascara had run a little. The black feathers on her hat fluttered in the breeze. "He was a drunk and sometimes a bastard," she said, with a far-away look in her eyes. "You know, Darla. You know my Jean-Pierre. But we did love each other, and in bed ... can I tell you?" Her blue eyes came to life and sparkled. "That man, he was hung like a horse!"

Later they ate ribs at the Park Avenue Grill, one of Jean-Pierre's favourite restaurants, and then headed home. Maria had a comfortable little two-bedroom rancher. They both changed into shorts and T-shirts, cracked open a beer and went and sat out on the little patio deck.

"So here we are," said Darla. "I bet you are exhausted."

"Yes, but I know sleep won't come. I'm all stirred up." Maria chug-a-lugged the beer. "So tell me, Darla. Enough of me. How have you been? How's life in Montreal? I bet things have changed, eh?"

"Too much. It's all changed. Though Montreal still has a hum. It's still vibrant and alive. But they say you can never go back, and you know what? They're fucking right!"

"So what have you been doing? Any crazy stuff like the good old days?"

"Weren't they good old days? We had some moments didn't we, kiddo? You know I visited Ginette in L.A.? Well, she is with the weirdest guy ever! Like, a big dodo creep."

"What's new? Ginette always picks weird guys."

"You know, you're right. Remember that Seventh Day Adventist guy with ill-fitting false teeth? Anyways, she had the girls over and they are all on this online dating thing. So I've been having a go at that."

"You have? Darla, you are brave. I don't think I will ever look for men again ... not for me."

"Oh, come on, Maria. Not now, of course, but given time. I know you loved Jean-Pierre, but in time it would be nice to have a guy in your life."

Maria took a long swig from the bottle and looked at Darla with a deadpan look. "Men, they want weird stuff these days. Look at that Weiner guy. That congressman or whatever. Taking pictures of his wiener and sending it everywhere. Can you imagine? And those assholes are all on Viagra. It's not natural. And these older guys want verbal sex now."

"Verbal sex?"

"You know, the girls at work tell me. They don't want to fuck anymore, they want you to put the wiener in the mouth!"

"You mean oral sex, Maria! Oral sex!" Darla yelled "Oh my God. You are the funniest woman on two feet." She almost fell off the patio chair, she was laughing so hard. "I'd forgotten how you swear. You'd make a trucker blush!"

Blush. That made her think of Lionel.

"Well, I'm not up for all that shit. I mean, I did a few weird … well, not weird … say, *odd* things for my Jean-Pierre, but what the hell, he was my husband."

"Oh, really? Cough it up—what odd thing did you do?"

Maria started laughing. "Jean-Pierre, he hated my bristly legs. I have the worst hairy legs and when I shave them and he make love to me, he used to say, 'Maria, your fucking legs are skinning me alive!' So I figured out what to do. I wore the nylon pantyhose to bed and cut the right size hole in the crotch. *Oh my God.* Did my Jean-Pierre loved that silky feeling. He was one happy man."

"You kill me! Maria, you are a riot." Darla was doubled over. "Oh, just hang on a moment, what about verbal sex?" She laughed so hard it was hurting, and she needed a Kleenex because beer was snorting out of her nose.

"You are one crazy bitch, Darla," said Maria, laughing along with her, "but I love you anyways." She threw Darla a sideways serious look. "I just want to say thanks for coming down for Jean-Pierre's funeral. I knew you would come ... you understand. I didn't want anyone else here. They would have thought I was fucking nuts."

Darla went over to where Maria was sitting in her armchair and put her arms around her and squeezed her tight. "It was one of the most memorable funerals I have ever been to," she said. "One I will never forget." And boy did she mean it.

On the flight back home Darla made up her mind. She was throwing in the towel on life in Montreal. Her job was only a consulting assignment, so no big deal. She was going back to Vancouver. She had been away long enough. Almost six months. She felt so much more balanced and ready for life again. She deliberately wouldn't allow herself to think of Charles. As soon as the thought of him came into her head she dismissed him quickly and thought of something else. It was working, and she felt he truly belonged to her past. She thought mostly about Lionel on the flight back. He had shown her there could be a life after Charles. Had Lionel tried to contact her? What had he thought when he realized she had blocked him on her Match.com account? And that drive he had

taken with Aaron to visit their father, had Aaron mentioned a crazy Canadian women visiting him? Did Lionel
now realize what she had done? She felt so shabby, and
the saddest thing of all was she would give anything in
the world to be sitting in Gibbys restaurant in old Montreal holding Lionel Stone's hand.

chapter 8

WHEN DARLA PHONED and told me she was coming home to stay, saying I was over the moon was an understatement. The great news was that she had found a fantastic job online with an Aerodynamics Firm. They loved that she was bilingual ... well, actually it was a requisite part of the job. And so, just like that, she could afford a cute apartment across the inlet from Granville Market. When you sat on her balcony you could see the boat traffic sailing up and down False Creek; a fabulous ocean tapestry view. Like that saying "the eagle has landed," Darla had flown back and had landed in a pretty comfortable nest.

I helped her get the necessaries. Lent her a bed and a dresser from my spare room. Gave her the bust of Beethoven back. I knew how much she loved him. She bought a cute dining table set at a garage sale and a bunch of stuff at a Hudson's Bay sale, so she was set up and ready to go. For our first real night out we had planned to go and knock back a few drinks at our old hunting grounds, the Sylvia Hotel. It is a lovely old hotel, an historical one, really, as it was built in 1912. It's situated right across from English Bay and at one time it was the highest building in Vancouver. It's covered in Virginia Ivy Creeper, which is gorgeous. When the sunset hits the Sylvia, the whole building glows a surreal red, and believe me, a lot of magic happens when that ivy glows red—especially when you've knocked back a few martinis.

Darla was already sitting on the patio when I arrived. It was one of those lovely early June evenings. Still warm enough to sit outside, with the promise of a perfect night.

"I've just sat down. Haven't even ordered," Darla said. She was dressed in white. White slacks and a white blouse with a purple and green silk scarf loosely tied around her neck. She had a knack with scarves. I always look like I have a hangman's noose around my neck. I have my own way of dressing. To give you a clue, Rhoda on the Mary Tyler Moore show was my fashion idol. The bohemian gypsy look. That's me.

"Okay, darling. What will we have? Are you in the martini mood?"

"I've just been told this very afternoon that I need to have a hysterectomy," Darla said. "So what the hell ... let's go with martinis!"

"Darla, you're kidding!"

"No. It's no big deal, like, at this age having children is in the distant past ... but still. Anyways, I don't want to talk about it."

"Okay," I said, looking at her and trying to read her mind. Since she had come back home I had recognized a big change in her. She was more serious. More day dreamy. I had gone through a catastrophic love affair years before, and I had never been the same since. It's not easy to get over heartache and betrayal.

"Ladies, what can I get you?" We both ordered our martinis served exactly the same. Vodka with a dash of vermouth, shaken not stirred, with olives. Lots of olives.

"I just want to warn you," Stefan, our waiter, said, pointing. "See over there on the horizon? There's a big squall coming our way. I would advise you to move inside in about ten minutes. We are in for a dramatic downpour."

We downed our first martini after asking Stefan to find us a table inside. When we were seated in a comfortable booth, I said to Darla, "Hey kiddo, look at us! I can't believe we are sitting in this joint together again."

"It feels good to be back in Van. It does feel like home, Di. Sometimes when you travel aimlessly, it makes you feel homeless even if you are living in a gorgeous place. Not that I was living in style in Montreal. I guess it's all about a sense of belonging. A feeling of acceptance. I tell you, the French have never gotten over Wolfe climbing those fucking cliffs and arriving on the Plains of Abraham. I mean, that was in 1759! Please!"

"That bad, eh?"

"Yeah, kinda. The Great National Divide. And as you know, I speak French." She shrugged. "But of course, with the *Anglaise* accent. By the way, I don't have that much cash on me. Sort of waiting for payday so I can't go too crazy tonight."

"Same here. We'll just sip on drinks instead of gulping." She wasn't listening to me. She was staring across the room.

"Good lord. See that man in the booth over there? Di, that's Father Joe from my old church."

"*Father* Joe? He's a priest?"

"Oh, I love him. The church is packed when he speaks. One of the most eloquent speakers on the planet. I should go over and say hi."

I looked over to see a man in his fifties, wearing civilian clothes, quietly reading a *Time* magazine. If he was a priest he was certainly out on the town incognito.

"Looks to me like he wants some privacy," I said. "Maybe he doesn't get away from the church too often."

"Really. Wouldn't hurt to just say hi."

"Would you order me a glass of red wine? I'll be back in a minute."

When I came back to the table, Darla was sitting with Father Joe. He had a polite, strained expression on his face.

"Darla!" I scolded.

"Come and sit down, Diane. I want you to meet Father

Joe."

I looked helplessly at the poor man. Robbed of everything he had hoped for the evening.

"Are you sure, Father Joe?" I asked.

He nodded curtly, still holding his *Time* magazine like a defensive shield in front of him, and I sat. I was a little peeved, well hell, it was supposed to be a special night and here we were sitting with the bastion of the Roman Catholic church. Not exactly my idea of riotous fun.

"Well, I have to tell you right off the bat," I say a little churlishly. "I'm an atheist, and as you are in civilian clothes I think it's only fair game. I'm just going to treat you like any ordinary man."

"Di!" said Darla, shocked.

"No, I mean it. So where are you from?" I asked.

"Ireland. Belfast to be exact," Father Joe answered in a lilting Irish brogue, and there was a twinkle in his eye.

"What a gorgeous accent!" I exclaimed. "You would put Liam Neeson to shame!"

"Diane!" said Darla, horrified. "Father Joe is a priest. Why are you talking about Liam Nielson?"

"Irish, eh?" I continued. "So what's your view on the politics of today? The Irish are always up to their neck in politics. What do you think of Obama and David Cameron? Let's get started ... and that buffoon Trump?"

"As a priest, I am supposed to be non-political, but if I wasn't a priest I would definitely say I would be for

Labour." He shrugged. "Or be a communist."

I sat back and sized him up. Up close, I figured he was about fifty-five-ish. He had thoughtful brown eyes and a weariness about him, but he was handsome in that craggy Celtic way. His nose was a little crooked, as though maybe it had been broken in another life. And his voice ... I was in love with his voice.

"Okay, in quick order," he said. "To answer your questions: Obama is a good man trying his best, Cameron represents the British class system or caste system, as I like to think of it, and Trump could basically be the Antichrist!"

I almost fell off my chair laughing.

"Di!" said Darla, giving me a warning look. "Jesus!" Then she looked stricken for saying "Jesus."

Stefan, our waiter, came to our table to take our order. "Red wine all around?" I looked at Father Joe's almost empty glass and realized he'd also been drinking red wine. "Maybe we should order a bottle, seeing we're on all on red. Cab Sav okay, gang?"

"Good idea," said Father Joe. Darla was still looking a little off kilter.

"Jackson Triggs Merlot is the special," said Stefan helpfully.

"Great. We'll go for that." I smiled benignly around the table, aware instinctively that we were in for a terrific night.

"What's your take on the Royal Family?" I asked. "Personally, I think they're a bunch of freeloaders. Why the British have put up with them all these years is a mystery." I felt I was on a roll. Well, hello. I had never been up close and personal with a priest before.

"The Queen is a good soul. I think the royalty helps to keep the country together. Helps the Brits identify with the nuclear core of the national spirit."

"And you call yourself an Irishman, talking drivel like that? What has the Queen ever done for the common man? Has she contributed to the cure for AIDS or education of the masses like Bill Gates or the Clinton foundation? No!"

"Aye, you're right on all of that, but here's the reason I do. There's so many dividing factors. Starting off with the basic ones like the Irish and English, Welsh and the Scots. Then Catholics, Protestants and Jews and a half a dozen other religions these days. As you know, the Muslims are the latest arrivals on Britain's shores. It's good to have some common denominators that you can call simply British traditions like the Royal Family, the British justice system, cricket etc."

"Darla has just come back from Montreal. She calls the never ending ongoing French Canadian line drawn in the sand the Great National Divide."

"Is that so," said Father Joe turning to look at Darla. "And what took you to Montreal?"

"Well, I was raised there ..."

"She was getting over a broken heart," I said. "And now she's back as good as new."

"A broken heart, eh?"

"Yes, Father. I fell in love with a man who was married, and he did leave his wife but ..."

"But?" Father Joe leaned back on his chair and took a long, contemplative swallow of his wine.

"But he wasn't ready, I guess. We lived together for only two weeks and he pulled the plug."

"My dear, you should have known better. Getting involved with a married man never works out."

"But he was unhappily married, Father. The relationship between Charles and his wife had been dead for years."

"Then why was he still with her? No, Darla. You trespassed on sacred ground. The marriage territory of another woman. No good will ever come of a relationship that starts off with trespassing."

"Excuse me for being a little rude here, Father Joe," I said, "but what in the heck would you know about love? About passion and longing? I fell in love with a married man once myself. So excuse me. If you meet someone and fall in love, how can that be your fault? You can't help falling in love!"

"You could make sure you don't get involved. What happened to your married man? Where is he now?"

I gave a big sigh and downed the rest of my wine. "I guess you have me there." I smiled at Father Joe ruefully. "I waited a long time for that man. I was crazy about him. Then when he finally left his marriage, he took off with another woman." Hello. I still wasn't over it.

"See? Nothing good comes from these affairs."

"Darla is trying online dating now. Have you ever heard of that, Father?"

"I have. I think as long as you're careful, it's fine. Make sure you know something about the fellow and meet in a public place the first few times. Modern technology, eh? Grand, isn't it?"

Stefan came up to our table accompanied by a young man and gave us an apologetic smile. "I'm going off my shift now," he said. "I'm leaving you in the hands of Jamie here. Be kind to him; it's his first evening working at the Sylvia."

We appraised the skinny young man up and down. He looked all of fifteen, nervous and a little twitchy, and sprinkled with acne, but then you had to be nineteen to serve drinks so he should be fine. "Okay, Jamie." I smiled encouragingly at him, "You can start by bringing us another a bottle of Jackson Triggs and maybe some munchies. Hmm ... let's see. Nachos would be good."

"Look at the storm." Darla pointed outside. The rain was coming down in buckets. "And I didn't bring a coat."

"It's a beautiful sight, though," said Father Joe. "Look

at that sea out there. Wild and frenzied. We live on such a beautiful planet. I don't think the average person appreciates it enough. Really, God is everywhere." He sang in a low baritone voice, "You raise me up so I can stand on mountains. You raise me up to walk on stormy seas. I am strong when I am on your shoulders. You raise me up to more than I can be."

A singing priest! And I have to tell you, he was one hell of a singer.

"What have we here? Bing Crosby in *The Bells of Saint Mary's!*"

"That's a Josh Groban song," said Darla, hiccupping "Bing never sang it."

"I know it is, but is Josh a priest? No! Bing Crosby was," I said, glancing over at Darla. She winked at me. She knew her singing priest had just scored another fan. I had to concede that Father Joe was indeed a contender, whether he wore the cloth or not, and I had to admit he was a damn good sport for putting up with the likes of us. And there was also the indisputable but endearing fact he was getting pissed as a parrot.

"So you ladies have been chasing love in all the wrong places. Chasing up the wrong trees. Slow down. Regroup. Just enjoy the moment." Father Joe's voice had that intimate ring used, I suspected, for only the truly fallen. "Open yourselves up to just the wonder of living. Enjoy the simple things. Enjoy being you. In the end I promise love will come looking and find both of you."

I felt a warm rush of affection for him that, in all fairness, could have been blamed on alcohol consumption. "Let me read your palm, Father Joe," I said.

"Di ... are you crazy ... you can't read a priest's hand. It's sacrilegious." Darla was visibly upset.

"You really read palms?" he said.

"I not only read them, I'm good at it. Especially after I've been into the wine or into the suds, as Darla would say."

"Is she good?" Father Joe asked Darla.

"Well, let's put it this way. Let me tell you a story. We were broke, like desperately broke, a couple of years back and so I said to Di, 'We should put an ad in the *Georgia Straight* and charge big bucks for palm readings.' She didn't want anything to do with it. Had only read for fun before. But anyways, desperation makes criminals of us all, or whatever the quote is, and so I went ahead and put the ad in the newspaper."

"That's not the all of it." I turned to face Father Joe. "She put in the ad that I, me, Madame Diane, was a world-famous Welsh psychic on a world tour who had read the palms of Richard Burton, Jack Webster and a host of other dead people who couldn't accuse me of lying."

"Well, we were a hit," Darla said. "We had so many calls. I would take the callers' birthdates down and Di would look up their horoscope and try to get a handle on what to say to them."

"I was scared to death when we first started. I had to sit in Darla' bedroom, Father Joe, and I would hear the knock on her apartment door and Darla saying, 'Come in. I'll take you through to Madame Diane,' and there I would be sitting on the bed with my knees knocking. Yes, the world-famous psychic sitting on a bed, how phony was that."

"Oh dear Lord." Father Joe was rumbling with laughter. "Madame Diane from Wales, was it?"

"The first time I did a reading, Darla took the money, ran to the nearest liquor store, raced back before client number two arrived and poured me a stiff one ... I think it was vodka. 'Knock this back,' she said, 'you look like you're going to faint!'"

"How did all this palm-reading business get started? I mean, it's not the usual thing people get into."

"It was the strangest thing, Father Joe. I had always been fascinated, even as a child, and had taken books out of the library. Learned the common lines, you know the life line and the line of destiny etc. So I started reading people's palms for fun. Big hit at parties and such. A big lark. But this one day I was having lunch with a friend, more a liquid lunch as we would say, and this man was sitting across from us quietly staring out of the window, lost in thought. I had such a compulsion to read his palm, and I finally said, 'Sir, I know this an odd request, but could I read your palm?' He was startled, but nodded and said, 'Sure.' Well, when I looked at his palm I was intrigued and started telling him what I saw. I said, 'I don't know how to explain this, sir, but it's like you have been surrounded by cotton wool for the last few months. You haven't been able to see, or hear or talk. Believe me, I felt totally stupid saying that. It didn't make sense. He took his hand away and said, 'Unbelievable.' He looked frightened, actually. He said, 'How could you possibly know this? I'm recovering from an serious accident. I have been in a coma for months. I'm still actually a patient.' He pointed to his hospital ID bracelet that had been hidden under his jacket. We were in a restaurant across from the Vancouver General Hospital. It was then I knew, really knew, I could read palms."

"Okay, you've sold me, Madame Diane. Let's give it a go." Father Joe offered me his palm.

"Father! Di! I can't witness this," said Darla. "To me, it's just wrong." There was a massive crack of thunder outside. The Sylvia's windows rattled. Darla jumped to her feet and looked nervously at the ceiling as though a bolt of lightning symbolizing God's wrath was about to strike us. "I'll sit over there until you're done." She fled to the other side of the restaurant and sat in a far booth with her hands over her ears.

"Isn't she a riot?" I asked.

"I'm not sure if riot tis the right word." Father Joe cocked his head to one side and gave a lopsided grin. "Maybe tornado. Hurricane?"

"Hurricane sorta nails it. Hmm ..." I said, looking at Father Joe's hand.

"Come on, give it to me."

"Looks like you've been fighting demons all your life."

"You could say that's a good job description for a priest."

"Well, your childhood was a mess. I guess it was hard times in Ireland back then." I could see the marks of pain and also the black mark of impending disaster. I looked into the deep brown of Father Joe's eyes.

"Come on, give it your best shot."

I fidgeted on my chair. Why the hell had I started this? "You've had a very different life, full of challenges ... even torturous, one might say. Like, what happened when you were around twentyish. I see a big break there. Did you run away and join the Foreign Legion?"

"Not quite. I had a Che Guevara in *The Motorcycle Diaries* moment. I took off to explore life."

"You went to England?"

"England?" He laughed. "No. I came to America. Where the streets were supposed to be paved with gold. I guess I was trying to find myself."

"And did you? Find yourself?"

"I suppose so. In a way."

"Did you work with lepers or start a revolution?"

"Not quite. I worked with drug addicts in San Francisco. The AIDS epidemic was in full swing ... The end of it was, I went back to Ireland and became a priest."

I took a deep breath. "So let's see ... the really bad times were when you were around ten or eleven ... somewhere in there you were sexually abused and that totally fucked you up. Like, forever." He didn't flinch or pull his hand away.

"And now. What do you see now?

"You're ill, Father Joe. I'm sure you must know that. Maybe a year left?"

"That's what they tell me." His eyes, wise and kind, connected with mine for a moment, then looked away. He patted my arm. "You're pretty good, I must say."

"So now what?"

"I'll be going back to Ireland in a couple of months. I'd sort of like to be there at the end."

"Sorry I said earlier you didn't know anything about love, passion and longing. You're probably the most compassionate person I've met in a long time."

He leaned towards me and I thought he was going to kiss me, and like an idiot I pursed my lips. I think I might have actually closed my eyes, but he was aiming to peck my cheek. Wine can make fools of us all.

"Can I come back now?" called Darla from across the

bar.

"Yes," we both shouted back.

Jamie came and stood in front of us and quite bravely stated, "I'm so sorry, but I think you have missed last call."

"The last call," said Darla. "You never said anything about a last call. Don't you know you have to inform us of something important like that?"

"Sorry."

"Young man, sorry nothing, get back to that bar and get us a bottle of red! Like, right now!"

"But ... the law ..." said Jamie stammering.

"No buts ... for God's sakes, don't you *know*," Darla flayed her arm dramatically in the air, her blue eyes blazing, "this is a PRIEST!!!"

Jamie scuttled back to the bowels of the bar. Three minutes later he arrived and silently put the bottle down on the table and turned and left. Ah, the power of the Roman Catholic Church ...

"That boy needs to get a sense of humour," said Darla.

We tucked in, happily splashed wine into our glasses and smashed them together.

"To appreciating the little things of life," I said.

"He could have brought us clean glasses," grumbled Darla.

"Stop complaining, we're lucky to get served. Look," said Father Joe, "the restaurant's empty. Not another soul in here."

We looked around. It was true that the restaurant, and even the bar at the back, was deserted. We hadn't even noticed. I peered down the far end of the restaurant. There was Jamie all by his lonesome, slumped on a bar stool. His first day at work and he had to run into us. The poor little bugger was wilted at the end of his shift waiting for us to clear out.

"Jamie," I called. "Can we get the bill?"

We were all happy until we viewed the charges. "This can't be right!" said Darla. "One hundred and fifty four dollars?"

"I only have forty," I said, pulling out my wallet.

"And I only have forty-five," said Darla.

"Ladies, what are you doing? You've been drinking like there is no tomorrow and you say you have no money?" Father Joe was slurring his words.

"Well, what about you, Father Joe?" I said. "You've sure been enjoying the grape. Throw your share on the table."

"I didn't have that much. Let's see, I have a couple of twenties here ..."

"A couple of twenties. *What?*"

"Well, someone is going to be washing dishes in the kitchen." Darla was laughing, searching for change in her purse.

"You must have a credit card. Doesn't the Roman

Catholic Church hand out credit cards to their staff?" I demanded with my hands on my hips.

"You ladies may be fun but you're crazy." Father Joe said laughing.

We squared the bill up and went out into the night. The rain had stopped, and the air smelled fresh and clean. It was quiet and peaceful, like the whole world was sleeping, and except for the sound of the ocean pounding and ebbing back on the shore there was a hushed, almost holy silence. Father Joe stumbled in the parking lot and Darla just caught him in time. I held his arm on the other side and the three of us lurched towards his car. "Are you sure you should drive, Father?" Darla asked anxiously.

"I'm fine, my dear. This old car knows its own way home. I don't have far to go. It's been a memorable evening, ladies." He tipped his hat then half fell into the front seat.

We waved as his car edged out of the parking lot. "He could have offered you a ride home."

"No, no. I need the fresh air. I'll enjoy the walk." Darla stared contemplatively at the back of the receding car. "I'm worried about him. I almost said 'Father, you can crash at my place,' and then I thought, what was I thinking?!"

"You're right. He shouldn't be driving, but there is literally no traffic on the road."

"I guess if anyone has a Guardian Angel looking over

him, it would be him."

"Never mind Guardian Angels, you better go home and pray for your soul. Getting an innocent priest drunk like that!"

"Me ... getting him drunk?"

"You strong-armed that poor little guy Jamie for the last round."

We burst out laughing. Darla doubled over in her usual laughing position. "Jesus and Hail Mary, we are both going to hell."

I watched her walking down Beach Avenue with a smile on my face.

Later, when I was lying in bed, I felt the mix of life's emotions.

Life was back to normal. Darla was back home and we had kicked off the summer season closing down the Sylvia with a priest. That was a first. But there was sadness mixed in with everything else. I was so very, very glad I had met Father Joe. What a deep and lovely soul. But I had to say, the best part of the whole night was that the Catholic Church had bought us all a couple of rounds.

ChapteR 9

WE WERE SINGING along with Billy Ocean's, "Get Out of my Dreams and Into My Car." Darla had the radio blasting, and the car windows were rolled down. We were barreling eighty miles an hour down Hwy 5 towards Bellingham, Washington, Starbucks coffees in hand, and the sun was shining. A perfect day. Darla had just heard that Miguel was finally arriving in Vancouver in two days' time. We had to act fast. She wanted her apartment done over. I mean really *done over!* This Mexican surgeon was going to erupt in flames of burning love when he saw her place. First impressions are important, and this senor was going to get it from the get go that Darla was a woman of the world. How we were going to pull that off remained to be seen.

The infamous Macy's store in the States was having a sale. Like, the sale to end all sales. I had slept over at Darla's apartment, and we had spent the evening googling Mexican history and the current political scene there, gleaning any interesting facts that Darla could use to impress Miguel. We decided, as we knocked back Darla's latest addiction, caramel-salted Stolis, that Pancho Villa was our favourite hero. Especially, after we looked up Marlon Brando playing him on YouTube. Talk about smoldering sex appeal. Even inhibited me would cartwheel into bed with the likes of that heartthrob before he could even utter "Viva!" Now if only our Miguel was half that man! We had set the alarm for 7:00 am, jumped into the shower and off we went. Darla had thrust her mess of blonde hair inside an old Montreal Expos baseball cap. We were both wearing shorts and T-shirts and touting mild Stoli hangovers. Our mission was to arrive at Macy's as soon as the doors opened and pick up as many bargains as the car would hold. Every once in a while we would shout out to the passing world, "Pancho Villa!"

Darla was in a swing mood state. Bubbling happiness. The man of her dreams was arriving. Tall, dark and handsome. *We hoped.* His photos on Match.com were not that good. No close-ups and a little blurry. But in general, all seemed magical. They had been emailing back and forth for almost a month. He was a plastic surgeon. His two children were at the University of British Columbia here in Vancouver. That was a godsend. Trying to win over grown children could be a nightmare! His written English was excellent. He seemed really keen. Like, *really keen.* Wanted to meet Darla the day after he landed.

But then her mood would swing to anxiety and panic.

Her place looked bare. He was from Mexico, for God's Sake! Her apartment needed colour and drama! Some life pumped into it. And more class! Lots more class!

I was in charge of bedding, and I had to find a lamp. Darla was in charge of everything else.

"It's all going to be so lovely, Di darling." She was dreaming now. "You'll be able to come down in the winter months. Escape the rain and cold and then Miguel and I will stay up here in the summer. Mexico just gets too hot during the summer months."

"I'll have to find out about visas. I think you have to get visas."

"Oh, Miguel will know all about that! Now we can't forget to pick up booze from the duty free on the way back. Don't let me forget!"

"Do you know what he drinks?"

"Oh, hell no ... I'm going to get a bit of everything. Nothing like having a well-stocked bar."

I glanced over at her. She looked like she was in intense panic mode again. *A well-stocked bar?* Holy God! We didn't know the meaning of those words.

"Now, as soon as we walk through Macy's entrance, head straight for the linen department. Those Egyptian cotton sheets that are on sale are going to be sold out before we know it!"

The parking lot was almost full, and we just managed to get a space on the outer rim. Darla started to sprint to the front entrance. I waved her on. "Meet you at the cashier counter," I yelled to her receding back. I felt disappointed in myself. I should have shouted *"Pancho Villa!"* Even though I had been to many sales, I was not prepared for the Macy sale situation. Or should I say the Macy's Hell and Brimstone Sale. Most of the women there needed Prozac. They were almost foaming at the mouth. I was reminded of rabid dogs, attack-mode pit bulls and charging bulls. Thank the Lord there was still a selection of sheets. I fussed over what colour to choose, but I do have an eye for coordination. Now the lamp. I couldn't believe my luck. There, in full glory, was a knock-off Tiffany lamp glowing on the shelf. Reduced by 75%. I grabbed it just as a burly hand lunged out to seize it. I eyed the red-faced woman. She weighed in at least 270 pounds before breakfast and was dressed in sweats that must have been 4XL. You know the type. Linebacker shoulders and ham-sized thighs. I envisioned her marching and singing Russian Revolutionary songs. "Mine!" I said, then bared my teeth and turned and fled. Darla met me at the cashier with a shopping cart filled with two tons of stuff.

"Guard this!" she demanded, and took off again. Her blue eyes were glazed. There were down pillows, a white quilt with red-sprayed flowers, martini glasses, purple cushions, who knows what else. I was paranoid people would try and steal the good stuff out of the buggy. If people jostled or crowded me, I resorted to snarling at them. It seemed to work. Finally, Darla was back with another loaded shopping cart. "There goes next week's grocery money," she laughed. "I've bought everything and have about two cents left! But look at this, Di!" She held up a Diego Rivera print. A woman kneeling with a huge basket of pale lemon lilies strapped to her back. It was stunning. "Sixty percent off! I've hit the jackpot! *The Flower Seller.* You can't get more Mexican than that."

We laughed so hard as we loaded up the car trying to fit everything in. It was almost impossible. I had to hold so much on my lap, and then of course on top of everything sat the prized bloody Tiffany lamp.

"I can't see you! Where the hell are you?" Darla kept laughing as she drove. Then the car stopped. What the hell for? I heard the door slam, but I couldn't see anything. What was she doing now? I waited impatiently. It seemed like forever and then the back car door opened and I heard a lot of straining and pushing going on. "What the fuck are you doing?" I cried in a muffled voice. Suddenly, the magnificent whole head of a palm tree was thrust beside my head. When she sat back in the car, I yelled, "You're nuts! Nuts! Don't stop again. I'm warning you. I am suffocating!"

"Sorry kiddo, but it was standing on the sidewalk, right in front of the plant store, with a big honking for sale sign hanging around its neck." She shouted, "*Pancho*

Villa!" as the car screeched off and all I could hear was her laughter pealing on the other side of the palm.

By the time we unloaded the car and carried everything up to the apartment we were done like dinner.

"I think I am too tired to drink," I croaked.

"Come on, kiddo. I'll just make us one."

I lay back on the couch sipping a Captain Morgan rum and coke. We were both too tired to talk. I woke up in the middle of the night still on the couch. Darla had covered me with a blanket and a pillow had been pushed under my head. Guess I had just crashed. The room was full of unfamiliar shadows. Unwrapped packages and mysterious shapes. Was that a palm tree over there? Oh, yes. I remembered now. Well, we had done it! The magical transformation was about to take place. Mexico, here I come. I was going to have to learn Spanish. Maybe the Rosetta Stone was the best way. It was all going to be too perfect for words. My face had a big happy smile as I fell back asleep. My last worried thought before deep sleep took over was ... had we remembered to buy tequila?

Okay. Everything was ready. Darla took one last satisfied look in the mirror. Red lipstick today. Her hair was down, framing her face. The knock-off Marilyn Monroe white dress from The Seven Year Itch looked stunning. That had been such a find. The martini glasses were on ice. The new nutmeg sheets had been fitted on the bed, and the light melon pillowcases contrasted beautifully, just as Di had said they would. Elegant. Candles subtly placed. Twenty tealight candles were alight on the balcony. He should be here any minute. She felt an anxiety stomach ache coming on. Should she pour herself a drink? One drink wouldn't hurt. She was contemplating a martini or a white wine when the phone rang.

"Darla? Miguel here. I *sink* I am just a *leettle* lost."

She stood a bit shell-shocked, staring at the receiver for a moment. *What in the name of glory was that voice? So high-pitched and nasal.* "You're lost? Like, where are you?"

"I *sink* I am on your street but so many apartments. Darla, which one?"

"Didn't the cab drop you off right outside?"

"Se cab? Oh no, dear lady. I took the bus?"

He took a bus?

"Okay, Miguel." She felt a little dizzy for a second and took a deep breath. "Yes, you are right ... lots of apartments, but mine is set back a little and has big letters. I mean big numbers. 999 above the entrance door."

"Now I see. I'm across the road. I will be there directly, my darling."

She leaned against the wall for a moment, digesting the implications of "dear lady, I took the bus" then dashed across the room, splashed a healthy slug of vodka into a glass and knocked it back. He was a doctor. A plastic surgeon. Plastic surgeons didn't take busses. Did they?

And that falsetto voice. That voice left her speechless.

When she opened the door she still wasn't prepared for the mirage standing in front of her. He was at the most 5′ 7″ tall. He did have on a well cut dark suit and a dashing crimson tie. He gave her a huge smile displaying perfect white teeth, made whiter, she guessed, against the olive of his skin. He bowed low then took her hand and kissed it. A scent something like Old Spice hovered in the air. She stood staring at him, mesmerized, almost open-mouthed. He was quite good-looking, but he had a ridiculous kiss curl in the middle of his forehead. Her grandfather used to have one back in the time of vampires. Men just didn't do that anymore. Well, maybe she was about to find out that in Mexico they did. She wobbled on her heels ... was it the vodka or shock? ... as she ushered him into the living room, saying brightly, "Are you up for a drink before dinner?" She waved a nonchalant hand at the well-stocked bar.

"Oh Darla, dearest, didn't I tell you? I don't drink."

She stared at him standing there in the middle of her living-room for a long, silent, contemptuous moment. The one reserved solely for teetotalers. "Well, I definitely think I'll have one." She yanked a martini glass from the freezer, threw in some crushed ice, and filled it to the brim with Grey Goose. Left room for the four drops of Cinzano. Stirred and took a massive gulp. "Here's to life and laughter."

He certainly was giving her the once over, from her silver sling back sandals to the top of her hair, unabashedly lingering on the cleavage.

She flourished an expansive arm to the open French doors. "Please go sit on the balcony, Miguel. Make yourself at home. Enjoy the view. I've prepared a few little appetizers for us. In lieu of a drink would you care for tea, coffee or maybe a glass of water?"

"Water would be *perfecto!* It is so hot. Se bus was so crowded." She cringed. *That voice!*

She placed the smoked salmon, rye thins, thinly sliced cucumbers, prawns and seafood dip on the patio glass table with the newly purchased Macy's blue linen napkins and silver cocktail forks.

Miguel certainly was thirsty. He downed the whole glass of water and then sat back and seemed to contemplate the food. He gave her an apologetic, quizzical look. "Darla, you have made so much trouble. I am so sorry to say, my poor darling, I am allergic to seafood. Of course I did not think to mention this. Our first date."

Darla popped a shrimp in her mouth. Then, without saying a word, she picked up the brightly flowered Mediterranean appetizer platter and grimly marched back into the kitchen. She covered the whole dish with Glad cling wrap and rammed the platter back into the fridge. *Shit. She hoped she hadn't chipped the plate.* She stared through the open French windows at Miguel. He was lounging against the balcony rail silhouetted by candlelight. He smiled radiantly at her and gave a small royal-like wave. As she poured herself another martini she half-hissed under her breath, "Hail Mary and Sweet Jesus! Let's just get this high-pitched squeaky-voiced short-stop of a little bastard out of here."

Thankfully, she had reserved a quiet corner spot in this seaside restaurant. Who knew what the night was going to bring? She listened to Miguel fussing and clucking over the menu choices. What a Dodo bird! He was everything she had not expected. Finally, he settled on roasted quail and salad. *Quail.* She ordered her favourite rib eye steak, a loaded baked potato, and arugula salad. When a girl is asked out for dinner she has to eat! *Plus, hadn't she just spent the grocery money?* She was feeling buzzed from the martinis but had reached the point where she didn't give a flying fuck! Alcohol could be a girl's best friend in situations like this. "Bring a bottle of red, darling," she instructed the waitress, who couldn't keep her eyes off the kiss curl. Darla guessed in life there was always the novelty of seeing something for the first time that caused one's eyebrows to rise.

She struggled to regain her equilibrium. Sure, Miguel was not what she had expected, but she shouldn't be rude to the poor man. She had never been accused of being boorish. She was better than this. Come on! Why not show off her homework? "I must say, I love Mexico.

I've been to Yelapa and Acapulco. Mexican people are so friendly. Very welcoming."

"I am happy you say that. And I feel the same about Vancouver. I know a little of your city. I was here as a student many years ago for one year. Very good year for me."

"Really! Well, you will see many changes."

"But I always remembered how beautiful Vancouver was. In those days my friend and I shared a car. He had it for his courses in the morning and I had it from 1:00 pm on. Crazy, but it worked. Of course, for the evenings we fought or flipped a coin."

"Which neighbourhood did you live?"

"Near the university. Beautiful area."

"Mexico is so different. Like right now, Miguel, your country is going through this shocking crisis with all these missing people."

"*Tragico!*"

"What is your take on your president? Enrique Pena Nieto? Dare I say, a very good-looking man! Like, how he is handling this?"

"Oh ... you know our president! *Bueno! Muy Bueno,* Darla! He is a good man but up against the drug lords?" Miguel shrugged his shoulders. "The drug lords are the cancer of Mexico. They are eating her soul!"

"But surely it can't go on like this. Those innocent forty-three students missing from Iguala. How can people possibly accept such atrocities? Keep on living with horror like that? 100,000 people missing since 2006 … disappeared … vamoosed … gone!"

"I sadly believe, and the truth of it is shocking, but the drug lords have more power than our government. The monsters kill anyone in their way. Why do you think I sent my children to university in Canada? For their safety. That is why I want to start a new life here!"

Darla watched Miguel with interest. His dark eyes were flashing. They were a dark chocolate brown and brimmed with passion. Too bad voice box transplants hadn't been developed yet …

He didn't seem to mind she was getting hammered. In fact, after they had eaten, he started to open up and tell her about life in Mexico. Some of it she knew already from Match.com. He came from a wealthy family. Was the only son and had three sisters. It was important in Mexico to carry on the family name.

"So where are you working now?" she asked.

"Right now I am working for a Scottish plastic surgeon. Brilliant lady! Internationally recognized." *Had he said working* for *or working* with? "I also volunteer with Doctors without Borders overseas helping with the Operation Smile organization."

Darla softened. So he really was one of the good guys. She had donated to Operation Smile. Had cried when she saw the before and after photos of the children.

He pulled some photos out of his wallet and handed them to her. "This where I grew up. The family home. That's my *Padre y Madre.*"

The family home was a huge honking villa! And there were Mom and Dad elegantly dressed and standing in front of a large Mercedes.

Miguel leaned forward, two elbows on the table. "*Tu eres hermsosa,* Darla. You are beautiful! Maybe the most beautiful girl I have ever taken to dinner."

Well. She could hear Di's voice in her head. *You could get him to change his hairstyle. That should be easy enough. Living six months during the winter in Mexico each year would be easy to take. Come on! Especially if it meant living in a villa like Mom and Dad's.* But, but, but. Could she ever in a million years get used to that Jerry Lewis falsetto voice?

"Yes. Plastic surgery makes a difference in so many lives. I've even had some work done on my own face. I recommend it."

"*You* had plastic surgery?" She stared at Miguel curiously, itching to check if he had tell-tale scars behind his ears.

"Why not? If it makes you feel younger, why not? My reconstruction is still not finished ... I have a scar," he pointed to his forehead, "I have a procedure booked to remove."

So was that was the reason for the ridiculous kiss curl?

"So how long were you married, Darla?"

"Long enough," said Darla.

"I was married to a wonderful woman for twenty-four years."

"Well, I knew you had been married. You said in one of your emails. So did you guys get divorced?"

"No. Divorce? Never! My wife had wanted a separation. But I am a Catholic."

"So what happened? You are apart? Right?"

Miguel casually leaned back on his chair, chewing on a toothpick. "My dear wife was murdered." He might as well have said, "My wife was a good cook," the words had so casually slipped from his lips.

Darla set down her wine glass with a thump. "*Murdered!* Holy God! Are you for real? What happened?"

"She was found in our home by the maid. The throat cut."

Darla stared at him in horror. *The throat cut?* "Who in the hell killed her?"

Miguel leaned back on his chair. A moment's silence. Then he shook his head gravely. "We never found out."

"You mean ... *the killer* is still on the loose?"

"*Tragico, si!*

"*Miguel!* Why haven't you mentioned this before?"

"Dear Senorita, these things are not easy to speak about."

Darla leaned back on her chair, staring at him in disbelief. He was watching her carefully. His fingers drumming a soft little beat on the table. He picked up the white napkin and dabbed his lips.

Surgeons had access to scalpels.

They walked back to her apartment. There were many awkward silences before she bid him goodnight.

She sat for a long time on the couch in the semi-darkness staring at the Diego Rivera print. Nothing was adding up. Or was it? His wife had wanted to leave him. No divorce for Catholics. No money for a cab. His bank account had probably been frozen. His plastic surgery. The blurry Match.com photos. He probably didn't look like his old self anymore. The scar on his forehead. His wife had probably marked him as she fought for her life. He had fled Mexico before the police could zone in on him. Money ... he had plenty enough money to bribe a cop in Mexico. He wanted to start a new life. Here in Canada. Fond memories of his student life here.

She gave a huge shuddering sigh as she turned off the dim light shed by the Tiffany lamp. Maybe her imagination was getting the best of her. But she didn't think so. Then she slowly climbed the stairs to her bedroom and slid her off her *Seven Year Itch* dress. It fell around her feet along with her discarded hopes and dreams. She washed off her makeup and put her earrings on the dresser. The empty bed with the nutmeg Egyptian cotton sheets and melon pillows awaited her. "What was I thinking?" she thought as she slid into bed. "Seriously, I really didn't know the guy from a bar of soap!" Her mother had a bunch of favourite quotes. Always dropping one here and there. What was that one now? She stared at the ceiling, concentrating. That was it. "Arranging the world and the truth to suit yourself." Alice Munro. "You got me nailed with that one, Ma. Here I was thinking he was going to be a George Clooney wrapped in a matador's cloak and that little shortstop fucker turns up!" She burst out laughing. It felt good belly laughing there in the dark. "Oh my God, I might have to seriously think about committing myself, Ma. I'll tell the shrink I have the High Hopes Syndrome and it's playing havoc with my life."

chapter 10

IT WAS THREE WEEKS BEFORE CHRISTMAS and the whole
city was in that magical mood, Christmas lights and
Christmas carols piping in from everywhere, goodwill to
all men yada, yada. I had been busy making Christmas
fruit cakes, my famous Welsh sausage roll pastry was
done and already in the freezer, and it seemed everyone
was on a high jingle bell note; that was, except for Darla.
She just wasn't with it. Darla really hadn't been herself
since she had come back from Montreal. Sure, we had
had that Mexican caper. Would I ever forget it? Turned
me off Tequila for life ... of course, you know I'm joking.

But I believed there was something Darla wasn't
telling me that was bugging her like acid rain. Well, okay,
maybe acid rain is being a little over-the-top dramatic,
and of course, I do realize that Darla, on certain levels,
is a secretive person, but aren't we all? I have secrets wa-
terboarding wouldn't get out of me. Darla would usually
let it all out when we were yakking over a few drinks,
but this time the dam was holding. She had a wistful,
unsettled air about her, and unusual for our Darla, was

not wanting to throw herself back into the fray (the fray being online dating). I privately wondered if Charles was still emotionally chewing her up, so when she called me laughing about this guy from England coming over just to have a weekend date with her, I was elated because there was that lovable craziness in her voice again.

"He's such a unique, different person. Listen to this, kiddo. He designs bridges that split in the middle. Like the Tower of London Bridge. You know the type?"

The type that loved split bridges or the type of bridge? Answer on both counts: not really.

"Get this. He's living in the very house of the famous bridge inventor, engineer ... I don't know what the hell you'd call them. That's how obsessed he is. Anyways, he's coming over for a date!"

"Coming here all the way from the UK for a date? Is he barking mad? Aren't there any dateable English birds he can find in jolly old?"

"Who knows? What do I care? All I know is he's funnier than hell on the phone and I'm kind of tickled that he has it in him to traverse the polar. He's coming this weekend. I know, short notice. I thought you might want to come along with me to the airport."

"Are you kidding? I wouldn't miss it for the world."

I dutifully picked Darla up on Saturday afternoon around 3:00 pm as planned. I felt quite pleased with myself because I usually drive people crazy by always being late. It was a perfect sunny day. The snowcapped North Shore mountains sparkled like they were out of the setting of a fairy tale, pristine white as they were, with an overnight fall of fresh snow. Our bridge lover's flight was coming in around 4:00 pm-ish. As soon as Darla swung her legs into the passenger seat I gave her a serious once over and said, incredulously, "Jesus Murphy!"

"What?"

"It's your outfit. You look like the Queen of Sheba."

"Thanks a lot, Di." She seemed quite unperturbed.

"I'm serious, kiddo." I started the car and headed out.

"You mean you don't like my red high heels?"

"You mean your three-inch red shoes? No, they're fine, maybe it's the white fake fur coat. The ankle-length white, fake fur coat."

"Fake? So what? Nobody buys real fur anymore. You'd get booed or have animal blood thrown at you."

"Where on God's earth did you find it?"

"I bought it in Montreal and I'll have you know this coat cost me an arm and a leg."

"Well, darling, in the short description I'd say you look dramatic as hell—as in, a James Bond movie, *Escape from Siberia*! And in the other short description I would say it's over the bloody top!"

"Give it up, Liza Minnelli!"

I grinned. I was wearing what I called my Liza Minnelli black pantsuit. The only trouble was, I thought I looked like Liza Minnelli when I wore it ... after all, I did have brown eyes and the same short, spiky, black hair. But then, unfortunately, I started acting like Liza Minnelli. I knocked back the drinks like I'd been in the desert for forty days and dangerously flirted with weirdos. You might say it was a recipe for disaster.

Darla, completely unfazed by my unkind remarks, positioned herself at the arrival gate in what could be called a regal pose, and I stood back waiting for the drama to unfold. People were pouring en masse through to the international arrival area. I could see Darla hesitantly scanning faces as they passed her. I was only now realizing, bloody hell, she really didn't know what Kenneth looked like. At one point she opened her arms, self-consciously, half-laughing, as a dark, very handsome-looking man approached her, but he swept straight past her and she was left standing with her arms open looking like a Walmart greeter that had no customers. She turned around and gave me an embarrassed shrug. Then the crowd petered out. A few stragglers, then nothing. She walked over to where I was sitting, looking bewildered and a little hurt.

"I can't believe he's a no-show! I was just talking to him before he boarded the plane."

At that very moment Darla was paged to come to the customs office.

Darla and I stared at each other. What the heck? We asked the airport information officer where to go and started off.

"Let's hope our Kenneth isn't a drug dealer," I ventured casually. Darla glanced briefly over at me and gave me the death look.

We could hear voices outside the customs office door and knocked before entering. Before us unfolded a bizarre scene. We just stood there gaping. A cluster of uniformed custom officers towered over a little man that was a clone of a Dudley Moore. A perspiring Dudley Moore. He was well dressed in a beautiful cashmere jacket, but disheveled with his white shirt half pulled outside his suit pants. His tie was askew and his top shirt button undone. He had a bouquet of wilted flowers in one hand and clutched a peacock blue leather briefcase in the other.

"Are you Darla?" asked one of the officers.

"Yes," said Darla, staring at Dudley. The customs officers had ceased talking and were sure taking in an eyeful of her. She did look a little like a Hollywood movie star who had inexplicably lost her entourage.

"Do you recognize this man? He says he has come to visit you this weekend. Can you confirm?"

"Kenneth?" asked Darla unsteadily. "Kenneth, is that you?"

"Oh Darla, thank God you're are here!" slurred Kenneth in an impeccable English accent. He was obviously on the downside of a couple of in-flight doubles.

He tried to pull himself up onto his feet but made a poor job of it and sank abruptly back down on the chair. "I've been such a jerk. I didn't know how to tell them we met on the Internet. Seemed a little over the top you know?" He gave a little hysterical laugh then convulsed with a loud hiccup. "Sorry. Must confess I had a little bubbly on the flight." He gave the room a lopsided boyish grin, running his hands through a shock of hair. "I'm truly sorry, everyone, about saying I was here on business. Silly, silly me. Yes, apologies are in order."

"*Is* he here on an Internet date?" asked the hatchet-faced custom's officer.

"Well, yes, officer, he is," said Darla. "Kenneth, why didn't you tell them that?"

Kenneth actually blushed. "It just didn't seem, it didn't seem ... well ... you know." He stared down at his feet, struggling for words. "It just didn't seem top drawer."

Top drawer! I couldn't help it. I bent over and laughed my face off. That didn't go over too well. "I'll wait in the hall," I spluttered, and exited the room. Once outside, I leaned against the corridor wall and howled. One of the custom officers came out, giving the door a bit of a slam. He stared at me, shaking his head, poker faced. "Fucking Englishmen!" was all he said.

Five minutes later Dudley, as I had now resolved to calling him, came out accompanied by Darla. She towered over him like a scene from *Gulliver's Travels*. Dudley was in a really good mood. "Well, thank God that's sorted! Darla, darling, you were a real brick coming to my rescue like that. Can you imagine? Ye gods of little goldfish. They were threatening to send me back on the next plane." He stopped to grin at me. "Sorry for all the fuss, old dear. May I have the pleasure? Kenneth Galbraith here." He extended his hand, bowed his head and sharply clicked his heels.

"Diane Foley here. Pleased to meet you," I said shaking his hand. "Hope you don't mind, but I'm going to call you Dudley."

"Dudley ... *really?*" Kenneth looked confused.

"Don't *you* start!" warned Darla, swiveling her gaze onto me, her eyes blue fire. Definitely the Queen of Sheba at this particular moment.

"Well, ladies," said Dudley, hiccupping, all smiles bright as a summer's day. "This is my first time in Vancouver and I would love to take both you beautiful ladies out for dinner to the best restaurant in town. Spare no expense, let's shoot for divine decadence! And if it's not too much trouble, a restaurant where they know how to mix the best dry martini." He tap-danced a little as he spoke and threw his arms in the air on the word *decadence*.

Darla and I stood silently staring at him as if he were from another planet, then I glanced over at her and said, "Well, I'm in."

Darla put her hands on her hips and glared at both of us. Dudley clutched at my hand, and we stood there holding hands like two kids waiting for Mother to say we could have treats. No one could ever say Darla was a poor sport. She lasted less than a New York minute before she caved in and threw back her head and laughed. "Oh, what the hell! Let the good times roll. Kenneth, let's straighten you out. Tuck your shirt in and let me fix your tie." He stood to attention as she buttoned his top shirt button. "That's better. Okay, now where's your luggage?"

"Oh … in here, my love," he said waving his brief-case. "You know, change of shirt, a few toiletries and my unmentionables. I'm only here for a few nights."

Darla and I exchanged a high-browed look. *No luggage.* No wonder customs had been suspicious.

We linked arms on either side of him like Dorothy, the lion and the straw man in *The Wizard of Oz* and fairly skipped out into the parking lot. Dudley, seemingly, loved to dance.

"So where are we taking our little bundle of joy?" Darla was sitting up front with me and Dudley dear was sprawled out in the back of the car.

"The best. The finest," sang Dudley's voice caroling from the depths of the back seat. He was such a shortstop I could barely see him in the rearview mirror.

"How about Il Giardino's? It's close to my apartment. And the martinis are deadly there," said Darla.

"Sounds good to me," I said.

"Sound good to me. Sounds bloody lovely to me!" Dudley sang out like he was in a Gilbert and Sullivan production.

Il Giardino's is a lovely restaurant specializing in wild game and Italian food. It has a rich luxurious atmosphere and is frequented by high powered business men, visiting movie stars and anyone who loves a fine dining experience. Umberto Menghi, the owner, is a well-known colourful character who has a string of fine restaurants in Vancouver and Whistler.

Once we were seated comfortably, the waiter arrived with the wine and cocktail menu, Darla and I took one look at him and screamed, "Stefan!" It was our lovely waiter from the Sylvia Hotel. "What are you doing here?" Darla asked.

"Luck and talent," said Stefan with a smile. "Come on. One of the finest restaurants in town. Been here two weeks and loving it."

"We have a friend with us tonight from London. He's looking for a great martini."

"But we must have champagne first." Dudley had pulled a pair of eyeglasses from his breast pocket and was solemnly examined the menu. "Oh, splendid. I see you have Taittinger Prelude Grands," he said, looking up with a smile. "Brilliant. Ladies we must have a glass of bubbly to celebrate this glorious moment in our lives.

Waiter, a bottle of your finest."

"To love and laughter, and to two of the most darling girls I have ever met in my life!" said Dudley, standing for the toast. I figured he was maybe 5' 5", but then his shock of hair lent him an extra inch. He did have gorgeous, emotional brown eyes and when he toasted he flayed his arms around like he was conducting an orchestra.

"To love and laughter," we chanted. Stephan blew me a kiss from behind Dudley's back. I couldn't help wondering, uneasily, if he was remembering our night with Father Joe.

The champagne was flowing.

"To great expectations!" I said. I thought that was pretty clever. Now Dudley was ordering wine. Stephan and he chatted in an endless discussion with names and dates flying in the air. Finally, Dudley was satisfied.

"Well, I must say Dudley, you really know your wines," said Darla smiling at him. Then she blanched. "Oh Kenneth, I'm so sorry. I didn't mean to call you Dudley. That brat over there has got me tripping all over myself."

"No, no. I don't mind you ladies calling me Dudley. Not at all. As long as you don't call me Dud!" He threw back his head and laughed a deep, rich booming rumble. "I met Dudley Moore once. Great guy, funny as hell. And to tell you the truth, we did look a little like the Bobbsey twins.

"Yes, *actually*, at my cousin's wedding. My cousin Mike, worked at the BBC for years, you know on the show *Doctor Who?* Took on a big social life, met Dudley and they became good friends."

The appetizers started arriving. Carpaccio, West Coast oysters on the half shell, Dungeness crab cakes with a sweet chili aioli sauce, and the wine kept flowing. Now it was Darla toasting, "to men who cross oceans!" It seemed to me that Dudley was getting sober and Darla and I were getting tipsy. One thing was for certain, he was totally enamored with Darla, he couldn't take his eyes off her. She did look pretty amazing in her deep blue silk blouse with her blonde hair tossing around, and of course, Darla being Darla, was being sweet and fun-flirting with him. Now we were all standing and toasting to "the custom's officer that let Dudley in!"

"Okay, Dudley, tell us all about your love of bridges," Darla encouraged him.

"Oh, don't get me started," he said, his face lighting up, but get started he did, and I don't know if it was the wine, but when the stories unfolded about Sir Horace Jones and John White Barry who designed the London bascule suspension bridge, Darla and I sat hanging on his every word. Either Dudley had a magical storytelling talent or it was his British Oxford accent that made everything sound so interesting.

"Bridges connect people. Connect countries, even.

Look at the fabulous Oresund Bridge between Denmark and Sweden. You have a pretty great suspension bridge here crossing the narrows in Stanley Park. I've seen photos of it."

"You know about our Lions Gate Bridge?"

"You betcha! Wonderful engineering feat."

"Would you like to see it? We could go after dinner. It's not even fifteen minutes from here."

"I would love that. You probably both think it's an odd hobby, but I fell in love with bridges when I was a kid and we went on a family holiday to Edinburgh and I saw the Forth of Firth. My God! I thought it was magnificent."

"You'd go on overload if you ever went to Venice," said Darla. "Your death certificate would state, *Dropped dead from bridge over-stimulation.*"

Dudley threw back his head and laughed. "That's funny. I would love to go to Venice. So many beauties. The Rialto Bridge, the Bridge of Sighs. We should all go and Venice bridge together."

"How about our very own Confederation Bridge going from New Brunswick to Prince Edward Island?" Darla asked.

"Eight miles long of brilliant engineering. You Canucks can be very proud of that one. The longest bridge in the world. I must say, top drawer!"

"Not *top drawer* again." I said, and Darla and I bent

over with laughter. Of course, Dudley didn't get that one.

Stephan glided up to our table. "How was your meal?"

"Fabulous," said Dudley.

"Well, I hope you realize, sir, you have broken some child's heart."

"Whatever do you mean?" asked Dudley, somewhat offended.

"Well, sir, you did ordered a reindeer steak for your dinner. Santa is going to be a little short on his deliveries this year."

"I did what?" spluttered Dudley.

"You know, reindeer steak was your entree. With a red wine sauce? Cooked flambé? Minus the sleigh bells, of course."

"*Good grief!*" spluttered, Dudley jumping to his feet. "I think I'm going to be ill." And he bolted to the restroom.

I laughed so hard I almost fell off my chair. "That was pretty mean of you," I accused Stephan.

"I sort of suspected he didn't know what he was ordering. He was on cloud nine talking to you ladies. Sorry. Couldn't resist having a little fun with it."

We took a cab to the Prospect Point Restaurant in Stanley Park. Darla was a close friend with the owner, and we were ushered to a perfect table overlooking the famous Lions Gate Bridge. The bridge was dressed up in dazzling Christmas lights, outside the ancient tall fir trees stirred and the waters of Burrard Inlet flowed black below. We ordered vodka martinis straight up, clinked our glasses then sat there, three people feeling a closeness, a bond, quietly inhaling the holiness of the night.

We finished our drinks and took a cab over the Lions Gate Bridge. Halfway across, Dudley wound the window down and leaned out shouting into the wind, "Brilliant! Brilliant!" giving the bridge his endorsement of two thumbs up. Darla and I held onto his short legs to anchor him down. The taxi driver said, deadpan, in a thickly accented voice, possibly Romanian, "If he gets decapitated by passing traffic, I am not liable." What an insufferable putz.

We ended up at Darla's apartment drinking shots of Dudley's duty free Glenlivet malt whiskey.

"Have you had many online dates?" asked Dudley. "You're my first one, you know," he added shyly.

"Can I tell you stories!" said Darla, as she kicked off her heels. "Take a good look at that Diego Rivera up there." She knocked back a malt and told him about the Mexican doctor. Dudley laughed so hard he rolled on the floor.

"That's really the Rivera up there?" he pointed to the picture above the fireplace and when Darla said, "Yes," he kicked his legs in the air like a dog rolling in the sand. "Oh my God. My Godfathers!" Then he lay there quietly for a moment. "I had a really bad experience a few months ago," he said, still lying on the floor. "I was jilted. Actually left at the altar"

"*What?*" Darla stared at him in disbelief. I sat poised with my drink in the air.

"I don't really want to get into it, but I was so down in the dumps this chap I work with said try Match. He was having fun with it. Meeting interesting ladies. But I didn't want to sort of try it in London, so I randomly tried Vancouver." He pushed himself up to a sitting position. "You know, browsing through the profiles, and there you were, Darla. It was your smile that actually captured me. You have such a brilliant, welcoming smile. And I couldn't believe my luck when you said sure you would go out on a date. I have to tell you both this has been the most fun I've had since that day ... that day ... you know, the wedding."

"Oh darling," said Darla, getting down on the floor and giving him a hug and kissing the top of his head. "And our date's not over yet. Your plane doesn't leave for another two days. Put the music on, Di. Come on, we are going to *p-a-r-t-y!*"

I put on the music and Dudley and I danced to my interpretation of Liza Minnelli's "New York! New York!" Darla sang her heart out. Then we had Elvis and Stevie Wonder and Springsteen.

Around midnight we finally sent him to his hotel. Darla had a mysterious smile lurking on her lips as she poured us our final night cap,

"I bet I know what you're thinking," I ventured.

"Hmmm ... do you now."

"Something along the lines that sometimes in life, wonderful things arrive in small packages."

"You nailed it kiddo. Here's to our one and only Dudley." We clinked glasses together and smiled happily as a perfect night finally came to its end.

Two days later, on a sparkling crisp winter morning, Darla drove Dudley to the airport. She had shown him the sights of Vancouver with style. They had visited Chinatown, Granville Market, Stanley Park, and had taken the Grouse Mountain Skyride. Had even gone shopping on Robson St. They both knew there was not the slightest romantic spark between them but one thing was for certain, they would always be good friends.

chapter.11

I WAS FLIPPING A GRILLED CHEESE AND TOMATO SANDWICH, my ultimate lunchtime favourite—well, of course there is the ultimate, ultimate lunch ... martinis straight up with olives—when there was a loud knocking on the front door.

Who the hell could this be? When I opened the door, Darla came bursting in.

"Di, guess what? My dearest closest cousin Kelly is getting married.

"Yes, yes and yes. To this amazing English fellow. I am over the moon and guess what, I'm flying to London for the wedding."

"Holy smoke! This calls for a celebration. Let me see what I have to drink. We have to have a drink." I opened up the pantry door and fished around at the back where I tried to keep an emergency bottle of red. Not an easy feat when there were so many unexpected emergencies in life. Thank the Lord there was one lone bottle there standing in the dark shadows between the ten pound bag of flour and the five pound bag of spuds.

"So when will you be off?" I asked as I poured the wine into two glasses. "You'll have to buy a new outfit. Something dramatic and fabulous. Those British gals dress to the nines."

"I know, I know," said Darla reaching for the wine. "I am so excited. I have a month to get my act together." She tipped her wine glass and took a long swallow. "I've been in London once before, when I was doing the young and reckless European backpack adventure that everybody did it back in the day. I guess I was eighteen. Europe on five dollars a day was the book everyone was travelling with. Can you imagine?"

"It's wonderful, and you are going to have the time of your life. Why don't you go on Match and arrange for a date or two with some charming Englishmen? Wouldn't that be fun? They could show you around London. Show you the sights. Kelly and her fiancé Nigel will be so busy with wedding plans and entertaining visiting guests."

"Oh my God, what a brilliant idea! What a brainwave, Di! I wasn't even thinking ... you're right, Kelly will have her hands full." She downed the rest of her wine. "Okay, I'm off. FYI, there's smoke coming from a frypan on the stove. See you later, darling!" She almost ran out the door. A woman with a mission. Places to go, dresses to buy and British dates to arrange.

I threw my blackened grilled cheese in the garbage, turned on the overhead fan to dispel the smoke and

poured myself more wine. I felt happy. Like, overflowing. Romance was in the air. A young couple in love.
What could be better? But something was irking me. I
had a secret. A secret I was keeping from Darla, and my
conscience was starting to bother me. It had started a few
months back when the phone rang just as I was getting
ready to go to bed. It was Charles. Darla's old boyfriend
Charles. I was in shock. He had been drinking even to the
point of slurring his words. "I'm trying to contact Darla,"
he said.

"You have to be kidding," I had said. "You have some
nerve, Charles."

"Please listen to me, Di," he had said. "I know I
screwed up. I have been agonizing over it ever since. I
tried calling her sister in Montreal, but she told me to
get lost and that friend … you know, what's her name in
L.A.? The French Canadian gal … she even swore at me.
You're my last hope."

"Sorry Charles," I had said. "Please just leave her
alone. She's finally gotten over you."

"Is she seeing anyone else?" His voice sounded
broken.

"She is seeing lots of people. Goodbye, Charles. I am
going to hang up now." And I did. Since then he had
phoned every couple of weeks begging and pleading for
me to give a message to Darla. Was I doing the right thing
by not telling her? I wasn't a hundred percent sure. All

I knew was that Darla was happy. Laughing again and most importantly, willing to try and give love a second chance. But then, late last night he showed up at my door.

"Can I come in? Just for a moment?" I had looked him up and down and then searched his face. He looked haggard, and though he was wearing his usual immaculate suit and tie there was something sad and haunting about his face.

"Okay, just for a moment," I had said, and reluctantly let him in.

He stood awkwardly in the middle of the living room and handed me a letter addressed to Darla. "Look, Diane, I know I have been a heel and a bastard, but I do love her. I just sort of went to pieces when Darla came to Edmonton. I had left my wife only two months before and my boys had no idea I was seeing anyone else. It was to be expected they would be in an uproar. I hadn't thought things through. I panicked and told Darla to leave. But honestly, I thought we would get back together again in a few months, you know, when my kids had gotten used to the idea that their parents had split up. And used to the idea of Darla."

"What did you expect her to do? You tossed her out even though you knew she had burnt all her bridges in Vancouver. Given up her apartment and her job. You were a heartless ass!"

"I know. I know. Don't you think I don't know? I just

want a second chance. Please, Diane. Just give her this letter. I just want her to know I love her and always will."

So I took the letter and had intended to give it to Darla. But now ... now Darla was going to England, and I figured I would hold onto to it until she came back. No point in upsetting her and turning her into tossed salad before her trip. I had said goodbye forever to the man I loved. He had tried to come back, tried to build a bridge with me from our past, but I had been resolute. Even when he told me he had cancer. I had held onto the pieces of my broken heart and closed the door. He had died two years later and I was left wondering even after all these years had passed if I had done the right thing, because of course I had never stopped loving him.

CHAPTER 12

IT WAS SO EXCITING TO BE BACK IN LONDON after all these years. Strangely, it did not seem to have changed. It felt very comfortable and familiar. Darla thought to herself how wonderful it would be to live there. A truly diverse, magical city.

Kelly and Nigel had a rich social circle; so many interesting people. Nigel was the best surprise. Darla had expected a special man. After all, Kelly wouldn't have fallen in love with just anyone—but Nigel was so much more. As you would say, a cut above the rest. Such a charming and gracious host, and he had done everything in his power to make Darla feel welcome. He was going to make Kelly truly happy, and Darla felt blessed.

Now the wedding was over and Darla was looking forward to...big drumroll here... her London dates. She had dutifully scanned Match.com for suitable male profiles in London and couldn't believe the response she had received. She had made a short list and came up with three interesting men. She had chatted with them for the best part of her last three weeks in Canada and felt comfortable enough to agree to dinner dates. One was a journalist, one an ex British naval officer and one had worked in the political field most of his life.

Tonight she was going out to dinner with the political one, Andrew. Knowing the English reserve, she hoped they would be able to just relax and laugh.

As arranged, she waited on the corner across from the tube station, scanning the crowd as they came up from below and poured onto the street. Then she saw him: a tall, slender middle-aged man, well-dressed and complete with a walking stick. He was looking around anxiously.

"Andrew," she called, and waved madly but he didn't seem to hear her. "Andrew," she yelled at the top of her voice, loud enough to be heard above the roar of the traffic. Apparently, this was not done in London. Quite a few people stopped and stared as though she'd escaped from the zoo, but at least Andrew finally noticed her.

He darted across the road and stood, seemingly a little astonished at the apparition that was Darla. She was wearing her blue spring coat and had piled her hair high on her head.

He hugged her awkwardly. "My goodness, Darla, you look even lovelier than your photo." He tucked a bottle of French wine into her arms. "A little welcome to London, my dear. There's a great restaurant just around the corner." He took her arm.

Within minutes Darla was seated at a delightful restaurant, La Poule au Pot.

After the waiter poured the wine, Darla gave Andrew a smile. He wasn't per se a handsome man, but was elegantly dressed in a dark tailored suit and blue silk tie. His nails were beautifully manicured and he had a boyish smile—what Di would call a "Lewis smile." Lewis being Lewis from the *Inspector Morse* series.

"I am so delighted you are here," he began. "So lovely to finally meet you."

"I have to confess I felt a little stressed wondering how the evening would unfold. But now that I am here sitting next to you, I feel wonderful."

"Thank goodness for that. So how has your London experience been so far?" He had a delightful British accent. The kind that sounded like anchormen enunciating on the BBC news.

"I'm enchanted with almost every single thing about London." *Enchanted?* Darla wondered if she was trying to sound British. "I visited here briefly many years ago when I was eighteen. Too interested in partying then to appreciate the treasures of this amazing city. But this time I've made sure I made the most of it. I've really enjoyed the museums. Such amazing museums here. But enough of me. Andrew, you said in your emails you have worked in politics all of your life. There must be some fascinating stories."

"I don't know about fascinating, but certainly there have been stories." He looked over the top of his spectacles. His brown eyes were warm and kind.

"So?"

"I worked with Major out of Downing Street in the day as a communications deputy. That was one of my personal highlights. Major was an extraordinary chap. One of the best, I would say."

"John Major!" Darla croaked. "Andrew, how wonderful."

And so unfolded one of the most interesting evenings Darla was ever to spend. To start with, the food was fabulous and Andrew made sure the wine was steadily flowing. But it was his stories that made the night. Political intrigue. The stories behind the stories, vignettes about the Queen. And as the wine flowed, he coaxed stories out of her too. Darla felt delighted every time she made him laugh. Maybe it was the wine, but she felt he was the most interesting man she had ever met. Now he was telling her how he had been on a committee for arranging Princess Di's funeral.

"It was a terrible time here during that period, and I mean for everybody, Darla. She truly was the people's Princess. I've never known London to be so eerily quiet, silent, a city filled with the silence of sorrow. Quite extraordinary."

"I know what you mean. The same happened in

Canada. There was a mutual grief. She was one of those rare public figures like JFK that truly connected with ordinary folk."

Darla was working her way through her dessert, a banoffee sundae, apparently the latest Brit fad, when Andrew shyly said, "I'm not much at this dating game, Darla, but I would love to see you again. I will be in America, actually Seattle, in a few weeks. Any chance I could take you out for dinner? I would happily come up to Vancouver."

"Are you kidding? I would love that. It would be fun to show you around Vancouver. Let's keep in touch by email. Do you travel much?"

"Not really. Always been married to the job, you might say. My sons tell me I deliberately work to avoid life. Maybe there's truth in that. I woke up one morning realizing all I did was work and I was getting older. Life was passing me by."

"Don't ever say you are getting old ... say you are evolving. A Keith Richard's quote."

"Evolving. I love that. Okay. Let's hope I'm evolving."

"So are you ready for change?" Darla raised her eyebrows. "Are you going to start living instead of working all the time?"

"I'm trying. Look, I joined Match.com. That is huge for someone like me, and I am planning a trip across India on the Maharajas Express later this year. Supposedly it's luxury personified."

"I'd call it adventurously exotic!" Darla reached over and squeezed Andrew's hand.

"If I was really evolving ... like supposedly Keith Richards is ... I'd find the courage to ask a charming lovely lady, such as yourself, if she would like to be my guest on the Maharajas Express. They say a journey is always more pleasurable if shared."

Darla looked into Andrew's eyes and saw the wistfulness brimming there. The unmistakable air of loneliness. She knew what that felt like. She had spent time in that place.

"Hmmm. Why don't we talk about that when you visit me in Vancouver?"

Andrew's cheeks flushed with pleasure. "What say we have a special nightcap to round off the evening? Maybe a Napoleon brandy or a port?"

Long afterwards, Darla would remember the evening with the fondest of smiles. She had been wined and dined by a dying breed: a true gentleman and a scholar.

ChAPTER 13

DARLA WAS HAVING MIXED FEELINGS about her date that night. The thing was, she had gone out with the naval officer Peter the week before and just about had fallen in love. He was a tall, distinguished, almost aristocratic-type man. Dashing would be close to the right word. Darla had casually mentioned she loved martinis and he had scoured London for the best bar to take her. It turned out to be Harry's Bar, which happened to have the best vodka martinis on the planet. I mean seriously, you fall in love with that kind of man. Both his parents had been killed in a car accident when he was young. He ended up travelling the world many times. He married an Israeli girl and become a Jew and lived in Israel for many years. So many interesting layers to the man. He had two daughters: one was a lieutenant in the British Navy.

He invited Darla to this special event in Portsmouth aboard the HMS *Ark Royal*. Darla was to meet his two daughters. Darla ran out in a big panic and bought the most gorgeous dress she could find, had her hair done

and her nails manicured—spent enough money to sup-
ported a Third World country and psyched herself up
for the moment. Well, as handsome as Peter was, the two
daughters were equally less attractive, al la Cinderella's
stepsisters ... or Israeli Rottweilers, as Darla preferred to
think about them now. They hated Darla at first sight, and
she was taken back by their rudeness and open hostility
to her. Obviously, they weren't going to let their dear old
dad get mixed up with a blonde North American Goy.
It had shocked Peter too. He was openly distressed and
tried to apologize on their behalf. But really, what could
be said?

It left Darla a little shaken up. Peter had been a dream
come true. But dating at an older age when the children
did not approve on either side could be more than a little
contentious. She should know. Look what had happened
with Charles.

She wasn't really in the mood for another date, but she
had committed and didn't like leaving someone in the
lurch. Come on, kiddo. Date number three. And it was
Colin the journalist. She might be in for a lovely surprise.
They were going to have lunch in Mayfair. Mayfair! It
reminded her of the Monopoly board, and then he was
going to drive her to his home at Kingston-on-Thames.
She had been a little apprehensive about how far away
that might be, but apparently it was an ancient marketing
town that was now part of London. Only ten miles from

Charing Cross, Colin had told her.

As soon as she entered the restaurant in Mayfair, the maître d' approached her smiling. "This way, Madame, the gentleman is waiting."

Colin stood up as she came towards the table, laughing and opening his arms. "Here she is at last, the lovely Darla. Come sit, my darling, champagne is already on ice."

Before she knew it, Colin had given her a full-blown hug, a flute of champagne was magically in her hand and they had ordered the special of the day, *pot au feu*, which turned out to be a chicken casserole.

Colin. Well, Colin. He was larger than life. A little overweight. A mass of reddish brown curly hair. A booming voice and the most charming smile in the whole of London. He didn't stop talking, but that was fine because he was one of the funniest men Darla had ever met. Funny, funny, funny. He did accents. He did one-liners. And he drank like a fish.

"Have mercy on me, for God's Sake!" cried Darla, holding her sides. "I'm not only hurting all over from laughing too much, but my mascara is running."

"Drink up darling, we're going to toodle off to Kingston-on-the-Thames in about two minutes. I'm hoping the traffic won't be too nasty."

"I wonder what his house is like," she thought as she swung her legs into his car. He obviously wanted to show it off.

The house overlooked the Thames. It was small and old, but it had a lovely view. Very upscale, everything in England seemed double or triple the price of Canadian real estate. Inside it was disappointing—not what she had expected when you took into account Colin's flamboyant personality. Except for an interesting book-lined wall, there was no flair or fashion design concept here. A real bachelor's pad. Just plain dark leather couches. A big flat TV and a polished wooden dining room table. The living room too dark, with a lingering air of neglect. Very little personal touches. No photographs except for ... hold onto your hat ... a large autographed picture of the Polish president Lech Walesa dominating the largest wall in the room. Ye Gods!

"What's the story behind Walesa?" Darla inquired.

"Someone I really admire. I met him back in the day. He left a lasting impression on me. Just a humble electrician, and yet he had the balls to go for it when the opportunity arose."

"When you met him, was it for five minutes or did you have the chance to really talk?"

Colin laughed. "The usual when you hang out with me. We both got drunk, but I got the best interview out of him ever before or since. Just a great guy. Smarter than most politicians I've run into. Most politicians are sleaze-bags or social psychopaths. Believe me on that one." The whole time he had been talking, Colin had been wrestling a cork out of a bottle of wine. It finally gave a satisfying pop and he set the bottle in a wine cooler. He took down two glasses. "Here we go, darling. I've chosen a very good crisp white and I thought we should sit outside and watch the boats go by. Such a lovely way to idle away the hours. I wanted to show you my favourite little spot that I call home here."

The tiny patio overlooked the river and was screened on both sides by flowering shrubs. Darla sank onto a comfortable cushioned chair, and Colin set the wine glasses and the wine in the ice cooler on a little wrought iron patio table. It truly was a lovely spot, and sitting there with the warm London spring sun on her bare arms watching the mighty Thames flow by, she thought, "I'm so glad I came."

Colin had a different personae here. Calmer. She realized it wasn't the house he wanted to show off, but this serene garden haven, this little spot of paradise.

"Let's tell each other funny stories," he said. "I'm sure you have some good ones."

"Oh, I have lots," said Darla, wrinkling her nose at him. "Let me see. Here's a good one. You'll love this. This old boyfriend of mine had a lovely mother. The old-fashioned type. You know, went to church and played bingo and darned socks. Anyways, her husband died and after a few years of being a widow she met this nice fellow at church and they became an item. He started off being a boarder at her house, and she was glad of the extra income, and then they started a relationship. Now this guy, his name was Guido something. Was very quiet, hardly said a word. How can I describe him? He wore his hair like that actor in *The Lonely Passion of Judith Hearne* … do you know it? Maggie Smith was in it … I loved that movie."

"Bob Hoskins."

"Right on the money. Bob Hoskins. Colin, you are good! Well, he wore his hair like that. Parted in the middle and slicked down, actually looked a bit like Hoskins, always wore old-fashioned braces, dressed for dinner with crisp long sleeves shirts, wore those arm bands to keep his sleeves up, sort of good looking in an Italian kinda way. He lived with Mrs. Hewitt for ten years or more, and just sat in his favourite armchair reading the newspaper and eating her lovely comfort food meals like sausage and mash or roast beef and Yorkshire pud. Very quiet, uneventful life. Apparently no family except for a nephew in Winnipeg. Then he died. And the shit hit the fan."

"Ooh, ooh … this sounds like it's the good part," said Colin, standing to top up their drinks.

"It is. Listen to this." Darla gulped down some wine. "Knock, knock on the door one morning. It's the police. Lo and behold, old Guido was a wanted criminal, a gangster on the Ten Most Wanted List, no less! Dear old

Mrs. Hewitt never got over it. She had been habouring a criminal all those years."

"And he even didn't rob or kill her," Colin squealed.

"How clever was he? Met her in church, lived in her house. Nobody had a clue where he was. Never received a bill for hydro or the phone. What better place could he have found to hide? And a lady who cared for him and cooked him his dinner every night. He always had money, but we never stopped to think where it was coming from."

"I love it. Boy, I wish I could have interviewed him! I bet he could have told me where some bodies were buried."

"How gruesome is that? And I've been sharing Sunday dinner with him. Ye Gods! Do you really think he killed people?"

"You don't get on the Ten Most Wanted List for nothing, my pet," said Colin, standing. He kissed the top of her head. "Will be back in a sec."

He came back moments later with a delicious-looking cheese platter with assorted crackers and a small dish of pickled onions. "How's that?" he asked, triumphantly placing the dishes on the patio table.

"You Brits and your cheese platters. Look at this selection. You outdo we Canadians by a mile. And how did you know about my cheese addiction?"

Colin beamed and refreshed their drinks. "Okay,

back to storytelling." And storytelling he did. Sitting there in the sun, wine glass in hand, he was a master yarn spinner. He had interviewed so many interesting people. Hemingway: "Oh, was he something else. Another big drinker. Halfway through the interview I realized our roles had been subtly switched and the bugger was interviewing me!" Clinton: "Old Bill is probably the most intelligent person I ever interviewed." And so it went and the afternoon, really a golden afternoon, slipped gently away.

"Stories," Colin said. "Everybody has at least one good story, and I love writing them. Writing stories has become my life story." Colin shook his head. "Writing about other people's lives instead of concentrating on my own." He gave a short, mirthless laugh that made Darla turn her head sharply and scan his face. "So how do like my view here?" he said, quickly changing the subject and pointing at the river.

"It's a little reminiscent of the water traffic back home where I live," said Darla, looking at the vibrant river scene below. "Just think, I'll be home in two days." And suddenly, just like that, she felt homesick.

Before Colin called a taxi and kissed her goodbye they promised to keep in touch via email.

"It's been such a special delightful date," he said, helping her into the cab. "I just know this is not goodbye Darla."

CHAPTER 14

D ARLA OPENED HER EYES and squinted at the bright
sunshine pouring through the blinds. The sound
of seagulls screeching, the smell of the sea. I'm actually
home. I'm home. She smiled, and quickly jumped out
of bed. She had arrived at the Vancouver airport late
last night and taken a cab home. She had dumped her
luggage in the hall and basically collapsed into bed and
passed out. Now she whistled to herself as she spooned
the coffee into the coffee maker and took down her favourite Elvis coffee mug from the cupboard. A brand
new day. She needed to shower and get it started.

After her shower, she wrapped herself in her white
terrycloth bathrobe, and with a full cup of steaming
coffee in hand flung open the French doors to the patio.
The sky was a brilliant blue and the air was fresh and
warm on her face. Jaunty sailboats and the huge yachts
of the rich and powerful were scudding up and down
Burrard Inlet. With a little toot-toot the Granville Island
ferry was chugging across the inlet packed with people
eager to shop at the colourful Granville Island Market.

Such an endearing, familiar scene. Home. It felt good to be back.

Well, Darla my girl, you've been on quite an adventure. Jolly ole England and crumpets and tea and all that stuff. She couldn't help smiling. What a year it had been. She had gone from being so broken-hearted, devastated would be the right word, over Charles, to having one of the most wonderful years of her life. It was a big world out there filled with opportunities and experiences. All the people she had met, lovely, interesting people, through online dating. It was amazing. People like dear Andrew with his rich "this is the BBC" voice, and sweet Dudley, the lover of bridges and that wonderful hunk of man, Peter, even though it hadn't worked out. Memories. Some of them like a dream. And, of course, Lionel … but then she had promised herself she wouldn't allow herself to think of him. Even the Mexican doctor fiasco had given her and Di a thousand laughs. Sometimes after a few glasses of wine one of them would only have to point at the Rivera picture above the fireplace to set them off. She had sent Di a teaser email … "I have dated three wonderful Londoners … and yes! I did make love to one of them." Knowing full well that would drive Di insane with curiosity. She turned her head and listened for a moment. Was that her phone ringing? Yes, it was. She hurried inside and grabbed the phone on the fourth ring. It was Di.

"Welcome back!" Diane said. "I am so glad to hear your voice. Darla, you have to come over. Like right away."

"You have got to be kidding. I've just woken up. I was thinking I'd come over this evening and catch up on all the news."

"No, darling. It has to be now. Please, just take my word for it."

"Kiddo ... I'm too jetlagged. Seriously, with the time difference it is probably the middle of my British night. I don't feel I've landed yet."

"In the middle of your British night? Okay, then. How about I come over there? Don't fall back asleep."

What the hell was going on? It could be said that Di could sometimes win the drama queen of the year award. Darla put down her coffee, gave a big sigh and rummaged through her suitcase for some clean clothes. She pulled on a white T-shirt and a pair of crumpled jeans and drew her hair into a ponytail. She had thrown a full load of laundry on and was in the middle of compiling a grocery list with the word 'wine' underlined when the door buzzer rang.

Di did look weird. Well, maybe pent-up was a good description.

"So ... what's so important?"

Diane thrust a bottle of merlot into Darla's hands. "Pour us some wine darling. Then I'll start."

"Start?" Darla burst out laughing. "You are a nutter! Are you pregnant? Are you leaving for Vegas? I can't wait to hear the latest." She brought a glass of wine over to Di, who was pacing up and down, and then went and poured herself another coffee. She was not drinking wine at 10:30 in the morning.

"I know you are in the middle of the British night, but you had better pour one for yourself," Di said.

"I haven't even had breakfast yet!"

"Don't tell me you've never drank on an empty stomach. Here, have this one." She thrust the glass of wine into Darla's hand and went and poured another glass.

"Jesus, Di. You've got me worried now. Okay, let's sit outside. It's gorgeous out there. I might as well get the shock of my life in the sunshine."

Once they were seated around the patio table, Darla stared at Diane. She was biting her lower lip and looked ... well ... what? Excited? Wretched? "Come on, spill the beans. What is it?"

"I guess I'm a little afraid you'll be mad at me, but I was only trying to do what I thought was best." Di raised the glass to her lips and knocked back half of its contents. She held up two letters in her hand. "It's about these two letters, Darla, and I think when you read them it is going to change your life."

"Really?" said Darla. "Am I supposed to be scared

or happy?" She sipped on her wine. "Okay. I'm ready. Come on, out with it."

"How do I start ... before you left for England, Charles showed up at my door ..."

"Charles?" Darla started and went quite pale.

"He had been phoning me ..."

"He phoned you!"

"Yes. Several times, wanting a contact number. Where you were living etc ..."

"And you never told me!"

"Darla ... I thought it was for the best. You were finally getting over him and starting to laugh and be yourself again."

"You never thought I might want to know?"

"Please don't get angry. You're going to get angry, aren't you ... anyways, he turned up at my door, shocked the hell out of me, and begged me to give you this letter. Begged me, like on bended knee, so I relented and said I would give it to you when you came back from England."

"You've had the letter for over a month."

"I wanted you to have a wonderful time over there and not be driving yourself crazy over Charles again." Di's voice faltered. "Anyways, here it is."

Darla took the letter and gulped down two big swallows of wine. She turned the letter over. Charles's address was on the back. Her heart was thumping in her chest, and she felt light-headed, but that could be the wine before breakfast … she took a deep breath and ripped the letter open.

Dearest Darla,

> *I hope with all my heart you will read this letter. I just want to say I know I made the worst mistake of my life when I asked you to leave Edmonton.*

> *I think I was having a mini breakdown, but I hope I have the chance to explain all of that in person.*

> *Darla, I want you back in my life. I need you back. I am hoping you will give me a second chance. I am now legally divorced and the only thing in the world I want is for us to get married. Please, dear, phone me. I know we can surmount any obstacles that might be in our path.*

> *All my love, Charles*

She sat back in her chair fighting back sudden tears. After all this time he wanted her back. Darla sat there staring, re-reading the words written on the white page, and then looked back out towards the inlet where life was going on as normal. While here on her little patio, life was surreal.

"So?" asked Diane.

"It's just unbelievable. He wants me to marry him."

"I figured that out when he came to see me. He was so distraught. But there's more."

"More?"

"Like, lots more. Like, maybe more than you can handle. But good more, not bad more."

"For God's sake, you're talking in riddles." Darla knocked back the rest of her wine.

"I guess I don't know where to start. It's sort of like a Harlequin romance, but better. Much better. More like *Gone with the Wind*."

"Di, I can't take this. Just tell me, or I'm throwing you over the rail. Before I do, get me another drink." She handed her empty glass to Di, who scuttled inside and came out pronto with a full glass.

"So this guy phones me out of the blue," Di says, "and asked if I had a friend who was living in Montreal. He said he had gone out on a date with a lady from Vancouver. Her Match name was Moon River and she had told him she had a friend called Diane Foley living in the English Bay region. He wanted to know if that person was me. Oh … I can tell this is hitting a nerve, Darla."

Darla was sitting upright, wired, with an incredulous look on her face.

"He said he was desperate to find you, and I told him you were in England. He asked when you would be back, so I gave him the date, and then he asked if he sent a letter to my address if I would make sure you received it."

Darla knocked back half the glass of wine. "Did he

send a letter?" Her voice was a half whisper.

"Yes, he did! Remember I said two letters?" Di triumphantly produced an envelope from behind her back and
waved it triumphantly in the air.

"Oh my Lord!" Darla jumped up and snatched the
envelope from Di's hand and tore it open.

Dear Moon River,

*At last I've found you. I couldn't believe you
disappeared and vanished from my life.*

*I remembered you had talked about your Welsh
friend who lived just down the street from you in
English Bay in Vancouver. And you said that her name
was Diane Foley.*

*See, I was paying attention to everything you
said that evening. It was my only chance to find where
you were, and actually it turned out to be a great lead
because she was the only Diane, R for Rhonda, Foley in
the Vancouver Directory.*

*So, my beautiful Moon River, here is the deal,
the pitch, and the proposal. I realize these are the most
important words I will ever say to you and maybe ever
say in my life, so I am going to choose them carefully.*

*Do you believe in love at first sight? In soulmates?
In knowing after spending one evening together that you*

have met the love of your life? I didn't until the night I met you.

I can't believe you came into my life like a dream and then you were gone. I have thought of nothing else but finding you.

I have, of course, found out you had a date with my brother Aaron. I suspect you were having a little fun setting up a date with me. Is that why you disappeared on me? My darling Moon River, I couldn't give a damn about Aaron. He is a judgmental old stuffed shirt. The thought of you two on a date made me laugh. You probably shocked the beejesus out of him and good.

Anyways, your friend informed me of your arrival date and I will be waiting at the Sylvia Hotel in the hopes you will have dinner with me. I remembered the stories about the Sylvia and thought it would be a wonderful beginning to meet you there.

If you will consider spending your life with a man who adores you, and is willing to spend the rest of his days making sure you are the happiest lady on the planet, please, dear Moon River, turn up at 6:00 pm.

Love, Lionel

I watched Darla's face as she read Lionel's letter. It was an uncomfortable moment, but a dramatic, over-the-top moment. She was fighting back tears.

"Oh Lionel," she said, clutching the letter to her chest. "It's just unbelievable. Di, he wants me to marry him."

"I think you better tell me about this Lionel," I said, reaching out to touch her hand. "Like, Darla, you never breathed a word about him."

"I know. It's because I screwed up. Remember the Stone brothers? Remember how smart and funny I thought it would be to go and date Aaron Stone's brother? Well, the brother is Lionel and Di ... he turned out to be the most wonderful guy. I kinda fell in love with him on the spot ... then Maria phoned for me to go to the funeral. And the college wouldn't give me time off and I ended up quitting. So I came back home without saying goodbye to Lionel, the most wonderful guy on the planet. And I felt like such a heel ..."

I went into the kitchen and brought the Kleenex out. Darla was crying like a baby.

"All this time I tried to forget him because I thought when Lionel found out I had dated his brother he would think I was a real phony. I can't believe he's tracked me down. He wants to meet me at the Sylvia."

"At the Sylvia? You have to be kidding. When?"

"Tonight. At 6:00 pm."

"You mean he's here?" I said. "In Vancouver?"

"Yep."

"Good grief. And you say Charles wants to marry

you?"

"Yup."

We both sat staring at one another.

"A year ago I would have given my right arm to have a proposal from Charles. It would have been all I wanted in life."

"And now?" I asked, getting up to look over the patio rail. Boy, this was intense.

"I loved him so much, Di. You know. But he truly broke my heart. This trip to London opened my eyes so much. I met some wonderful guys. Real one-of-a-kind types. I have some great stories for you. And there may be many jerks out there, as we all know, but there are hundreds of wonderful, decent men. It's a big old world. Sometimes we forget."

"And Lionel?"

"Lionel is like feeling love for the first time. I really don't know him. For God's sake, we had one date. But it was magical. It was the closest thing to heaven. Remember when I first came home, how you kept asking me, 'what's wrong'? It was all about Lionel. I was so upset I had messed up at my big chance at love. He really is a beautiful man. What on God's green earth do I do?"

"I don't know," I said, turning to look at her. She sat with Lionel's letter still clutched to her breast.

"Well, what would you do?"

"What would I do? Jumping Jesus, what would I do?

Of course only you, Darla, could find yourself in such a spot. Go back to the old or choose the new?"

I turned back to the rail, to the hustle bustle of the world, to the loveliness of the inlet with the little ferries chugging back and forth and the sailboats heading for the wide open sea. I opened up my arms and cried out to anyone who would care to listen. "What would you do? We need an answer before 6:00 pm tonight!"

EPILOGUE

EVEN THOUGH THERE ARE OVER 91 MILLION PEOPLE using internet dating sites, which means this form of dating is widely popular and accepted, I still get comments from people who say they feel intimidated by the process. "It sounds so complicated," they say. I get a lot of, "It's like hanging yourself out there bare naked in the public eye." Really? It's not at all like that. With that in mind, I've put together a few suggestions and some information that will hopefully make it easier for you in your search for a new partner and will give you a heads up on what to expect when you decide to try internet dating.

So here we go.

You will be asked for credit card information.

Should you sign up for one month, or three? Should it take more than three months to find a new man, maybe a husband? Be patient, it usually takes time.

You will need a *username.* That can be a little difficult because most of the usual ones have been taken as the sites are so busy. With a little time and patience you will come up with something unique.

You will receive more hits if you include a photo of yourself. Even better if you post a couple of photos. Try to be honest and choose fairly recent pics. I know we all think we look the same as we did ten years ago. Trying to scan a photo can be a little tricky. Once I was so frustrated I mailed a photo to Match at their address in Texas, with my username and e-mail address on the back.

They will ask your age. How honest do you have to be? Only you know the answer to that question.

Height? Well you can't mess with that.

Weight? Average? Above average? Full size. Queen size.

Status. That is an easy one. Widowed. Divorced. Single.

Distance you will travel to meet the love of your life? 5 to 500 miles? I guess that depends on you.

Now a more difficult request. Write 200 words to describe yourself. This is a tough one. You might feel like saying you are feeling bitter and angry and pissed off that you have to be on a dating site writing these words. Hating an ex bastard husband that has put you into a position of baring your heart and your soul on the internet. However, that is not going to help you one little bit. I found it easier to ask a close friend to help me with the words to describe myself. It is very difficult to describe yourself objectively. Most of us are too modest to blow our own horn. But do remember your interests, simple things like running, long walks with your dog, caring for a parent, make you become a real human being via the written word. Don't be afraid to be vulnerable.

You will be asked what qualities you are looking for in a partner. Of course you will want to say "a tall, dark handsome man with tons of money who will take me around the world and grant me my every wish." *Wake up and shake your head!* Dig deep and prioritize what you really want and expect in a companion. Reading other people's profiles will give you some insight. They could say, moonlight walks, going out for fine dining etc. but what does that really say about what qualities you admire in a man? Be truly honest and you will have more of a chance of finding your Prince Charming. Say what you really feel. It can be tough doing that.

Now you post your profile and all you have left is to sit back and wait. You may receive one or two or twenty people who will send you a wink or a short note. You can click on their profile and send a short note back. After a few exchanges you might feel ready to meet for coffee or a drink. Do not let it go too long because feeling compatible online can be completely different after you meet. The proof is in the pudding ... or in the meeting. The aim is not to waste each other's time.

You might meet someone you like and not hear from them again. Do not be disheartened. You have to develop a bit of a tough skin. There will be times someone will really like you and you instinctively feel he is not Mr. Right. It is always a courteous gesture to write a short note when that happens to let the person know you won't be seeing them again. Better that then to keep them dangling.

Do NOT under any circumstances go offline and converse on your private email. Your privacy is protected as long as you stay on the dating site.

Darla's Do's and Don't's

1. Honest profile.

2. Always respond after a date letting the person know if you won't be seeing them again.

3. Dress appropriately. Remember the importance of a first impression.

4. Do NOT give out your private phone number until you have a face to face meeting and feel at ease with your date.

5. When you arrange to meet for coffee buy your own beverage and then sit down.

6. Do NOT speak of your ex other than to state you are divorced or widowed.

7. Do NOT wait too long to meet. There are scams online. People can sound charming but there is nothing like seeing and assessing someone eye to eye.

8. Do NOT go off the protected privacy of the dating site.

9. Do NOT get discouraged or disheartened if things do not happen right away. Think of it as a job and be diligent in following up promising leads.

10. Above all, think of this as a brand new adventure. You are in the safety of your home. You are totally in control of to whom you will respond and communicate. Always remember most people are in the same boat as you trying to find someone to share their life. I believe most people who take time to go through the process are sincere.

If you enjoyed Darla's Last Kick at the Can,
please post a review for the book on Amazon.

I would love to hear from you. You can find me at:
Web: www.darla-darling.com
E-mail: DarlasLastKickAtTheCan@gmail.com
Facebook.com/DarlasDating
Twitter: @DarlasDating

S.D. FORSTER,

Proof

Made in the USA
Charleston, SC
22 February 2017